CONTRACTOR LEATHER

The life of JOHN TOWLERTON LEATHER (1804-1885)

HYDRAULIC ENGINEER AND CONTRACTOR OF

RAILWAYS AND SEA DEFENCES

David Leather

by

David Leather

LEATHER FAMILY HISTORY SOCIETY

Bid harbours open, public ways extend,
Bid temples, worthier of the God, ascend;
Bid the broad arch the dangerous flood contain,
The mole projected break the roaring main,
Back to his bounds their subject sea command,
And roll obedient rivers thro' the land.
These honours Peace to happy Britain brings;
These are imperial works, and worthy kings.

Alexander Pope (1688-1744) *Moral Essays*. Epistle iv, 1. 197.

[The word 'mole' in the fourth line carries the meaning of 'breakwater'. The last line is quoted on the commemoration stone laid at the completion of the Portland Breakwater by the Prince of Wales on 29 July 1872.]

Published by the Leather Family History Society 2005
Woodlands, Panorama Drive, Ilkley, West Yorkshire, LS29 9RA

© Leather Family History Society
ISBN 0 9520545 3 1

Produced and printed by Inprint and Design Ltd., University of Bradford

Acknowledgements

Thanks to the staff of Leeds City Library, and particularly to Ann Heap, who started me off on a long trail of research there; also to the helpful staff at the public libraries in Bradford, Wakefield, Sheffield, Chesterfield, Liverpool, Warrington, Widnes, Inverness, Wisbech, Portsmouth, Weymouth and Dorchester; librarians at Edinburgh University and Durham School; staff at branches of West Yorkshire Archives in Leeds, Bradford and Wakefield, Leeds Industrial Museum, Leeds Art Gallery, the Henry Moore Institute Leeds, Wisbech and Fenland Museum, Berwick Record Office, Newcastle Record office, the British Library at Boston Spa and the Public Record Office at Kew; the Royal Naval Museum, Portsmouth City Record Office, Dorset County Record office, Royal Exchange Art Gallery, London; to John Whitaker of Leeds who dug out information on Waterloo Main, coal distribution and railway contracts; Geoffrey Horsman, archivist for the Hunslet Engine Company who, at Leeds Industrial Museum, showed me the original order books of the Hunslet and Boyne Engine Works, and many of the working drawings of locomotives; John Goodchild and the 'local history study centre' housing the John Goodchild Collection in Wakefield; Carol Morgan archivist of The Institution of Civil Engineers, London, where I found research notes of Frank D Smith; Alison Leather for interpreting the notes; Mike Chrimes at the library of the Institution of Civil Engineers; Philip Riden, author of British Blast Furnace Statistics; Jane Shuttlewood of Southsea for information on the Spithead Sea Forts; Richard Clammer of Chepstow and Stuart Morris for information about the steamboats of Portland; Bob Rennison on aspects of Leather civil engineers; Gillian Bennett Historian at the Commonwealth Institute, Angus Watson Historian, Keld Fenwick of the Newcomen Society, Michael Conyngham Greene and Anne Berens direct descendants of J T Leather, John B Leather for information on railways, Dick Pettit for acting as editor, and Jenny Dixon, and John Forster for their valuable comments on reading the text. Thanks to Noel Watson for his drawing of Brindley's aqueduct and a big thanks to Michael Conyngham Greene for prints of family photographs and constant help about the family; and finally to Jackie Nichol for the fine layout of the book.

The maps and sections on pages 6, 19, 46, 90, 92, 105, 111 and 120 were drawn by the author. The painting on the cover is from J W Carmichael's 'Construction of Portland Breakwater', photograph by permission of the Royal Exchange Art Gallery, London. This magnificent oil painting, measuring 66 by 40 inches and on show in 2005, has a price tag of £140,000.

Most of the information for this biography has come from the public domain, from archives, libraries, museums, newspapers and journals of the day. All J T Leather's personal notes, diaries, papers and engineering drawings that might have survived, disappeared in 1945 when Middleton Hall was sold in the absence of the last Leather owner.

David Leather
July 2005

Contents

Three Generations of Engineers

John Towlerton Leather was a foremost civil engineer and entrepreneur of the Nineteenth Century. In his lifetime he was referred to as 'the well-known Hydraulic Engineer' and 'the Contractor of Public Works'. Although now unknown, his place is with such as Stephenson, Jessop, Fowler, Brindley and Brunel – names that recur frequently in this account. These men had the skill and confidence to design huge undertakings – canals, reservoirs, railways, bridges, docks, harbours and sea defences – and push them through to completion. They were men with vision and organising ability, who could overcome nature and change the landscape, men who believed in the future.

Miniature of John Towlerton Leather aged about 60.

John Towlerton Leather had the distinct advantage of being born into a family of engineers (family tree on page 4) with the corresponding connections and position in society, and he came along at exactly the right time. Two years before he was born – in 1802 – the great Cornishman Trevithick patented his high-pressure steam engine, the invention which heralded the age of steam. The roller coaster of scientific achievements and developments of the Industrial Revolution were rapidly changing the way people lived and worked, and JTL was one of those who seized the new opportunities with self assurance and success.

Our man was tall and slim with dark hair and blue eyes. The miniature shows a high forehead and straight nose, typical of many of the Leather family. He was a somewhat quiet and withdrawn individual, but with great intelligence, a flair for mathematics and problem solving, and the confidence to take an innovative line. His works include the design of reservoirs for Sheffield Waterworks, he founded the Hunslet Steam Engine Company, managed several collieries including his own, and contracted for three bridges and four sections of railway. His biggest projects were for the Admiralty: the Portland Breakwater, the Spithead forts and the extensions to Portsmouth Harbour.

It is amazing how much he fitted in to fifty years of his working life. For thirty-four years (1831-1865) he was chief engineer then consultant engineer to Sheffield Waterworks and was responsible for the design of seven major dams,[1] two of which stood 95 feet (29m) above the valley floor –the second highest then built in Britain. Six of them are still supplying the city of Sheffield with high quality drinking water and prove a lasting and useful legacy. Their design in the 1830s and 1840s showed a remarkable vision for the future.

When J T Leather got out of his chair and left the office for the contracting business, he was leaving the safety of the drawing board for the insecure and exciting world of the contractor. Although the Leeds Extension railway line from Leeds to York was stopped in its tracks, the beautiful stone eleven-arch bridge over the River Wharfe at Tadcaster

is a huge monument to this man. The sections of railway line at Chesterfield and along the Erewash valley are still in use after 160 years. The fine stone bridge he put in at Inverness was unfortunately dismantled for

Tadcaster Viaduct was built over the River Wharfe by Contractor Leather in 1847. It was never used for the intended railway and this view was taken 150 years later.

a wider one in the 1930s, as was the Wisbech Bridge. The fascinating thing about the constructing of these two bridges, together with the dam on the flooded fens of Middle Drain, is that J T Leather was called in when others had failed. He seemed to be the only man who could get the job done, who had the ability and the big ideas for operating on a grand scale that brought the projects to a satisfactory conclusion.

He was a great organiser, and if he needed half a dozen steam engines, a steam crane and two hundred men he knew how to get them. He rarely put himself in the limelight. When his works were reported in local newspapers, there is seldom a reference to him. If it came to speech-making and public occasions he kept in

[1] About the same time engineers George Leather and his son John Wignall Leather built dams for Leeds Waterworks and Bradford Waterworks. The three Leather engineers between them built 20 reservoir dams, representing 20% of all those built in Britain in the two middle quarters of the 19th century.

the background, but he took pride in his achievements and often celebrated them in great style, for example, with a dinner for his workmen or a special train for visiting dignitaries.

The three major projects in the south of England occupied Contractor Leather for more than half his working life and stand as memorials to a fine civil engineer who seldom sought publicity but was known and trusted for his sound and honest work. The Spithead Forts were a tremendous challenge for any engineer. These granite island fortresses rising from the seabed in 50 feet of water took all the technical expertise of the day to bring them to fruition. They were built to help defend the coast of southern England and, although they have outlasted their military purpose, they have been recognised more recently as the triumphant structures they are. They now attract prices of up to £10 million apiece as fortified island residences for the wealthy eccentric. The extensions to Portsmouth Harbour have become overshadowed by later develop-ments and are not so easily

Spitbank Fort lies at the entrance to Portsmouth Harbour, one of five forts built by Contractor Leather. This one was completed in 1870 and in 2005 was up for sale at £500,000. (Vail Williams)

recognised today. At Weymouth the Portland Breakwater has grown another arm and provides a lasting sheltered anchorage for naval vessels and other craft. This broad sea wall is still in naval territory but perhaps one day people will be free to walk along it as they did when it was being built.

J T Leather made a lot of money, acquired three country estates and a London home, and met the Prince of Wales and the Shah of Persia. But in mid-career the failure of one of JTL's high dams caused the biggest disaster in Victorian England – the Great Sheffield Flood. He rode the storm and a decade later was appointed High Sheriff of Northumberland, though he was never knighted. We start with JTL's grandfather George Leather, the first of a family of notable engineers.

George Leather (1748-1814)   George Leather senior had a great influence on the following generations and stands at the head of an enormous family. Born in 1748, he was the younger of two sons of a shoemaker. He and his brother Samuel grew up together, shared many experiences and turned out to be capable and talented. George certainly made his mark.

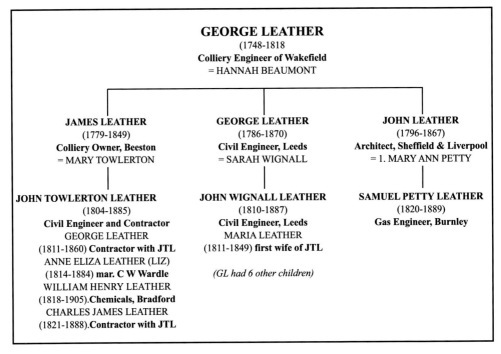

Simplified Leather Family Tree showing the relationship of the several engineers

In south Lancashire the old family home of Wood End Farm stood in the parish of Great Sankey on the east side of Barrows Green Lane, about a mile away through the fields from the village of Farnworth. The whole area is now part of the town of Widnes, non-existent in the 1760s, though the name Widnes does occur on old maps, more or less where the farm stood. Great Sankey village was two and a half miles away to the east towards Warrington, and the land of Wood End Farm spread out in that direction, a low-lying, gently rolling, fertile area, only a mile or so north of the River Mersey. The farmhouse must have been a spacious one, big enough for the family of six, with additional room for a guest or two.

When George Leather was a boy, the first canal to be built in Britain was being constructed only a mile or so from his home. This was the Sankey Brook Navigation built in 1755 to 1756 (now called the St Helen's Canal). It started at the mouth of Sankey Brook on the River Mersey, curved round alongside the brook, which supplied it with water, and continued past Sankey Bridge and Winwick Hall to finish in St Helens. Seven years later in 1762-63, when George was fourteen, Sankey Brook Navigation was extended across Cuerdley and Widnes salt marshes to reach the Mersey at Fiddler's Ferry, less than two miles from Wood End Farm. The main traffic of the canal was coal from the St Helens coalfield via the River Mersey to Liverpool and north Cheshire.

The Brindley Connection In the 1760s the Leathers took in a guest, the canal builder and engineer James Brindley. This was to change the course of the family history.

In 1759 James Brindley, the great eighteenth century canal builder who constructed 360 miles of canals across Britain, was hired by the Duke of Bridgewater, together with John Gilbert, to build a ten-mile canal to transport coal cheaply from the Duke's mines at Worsley to the centre of Manchester. Brindley's far-sighted solution included a tunnel extending from the head of the canal into the mines, and a very fine aqueduct, opened in July 1761, to carry the canal on arches high over the River Irwell.

Portrait of James Brindley 1716-1772.

The aqueduct was so spectacular that people came to marvel at boats sailing thirty-nine feet above the river and not a drop of water leaking out! The canal is still in use

James Brindley's aqueduct over the River Irwell, at Barton near Manchester, opened to traffic in July 1761 when people marvelled at the fact that boats could sail thirty feet 'up in the sky'. (drawing by Noel Watson from an old sketch)

today, but Brindley's historic aqueduct over the Irwell had to be dismantled when the Manchester Ship Canal was built between 1887 and 1893.

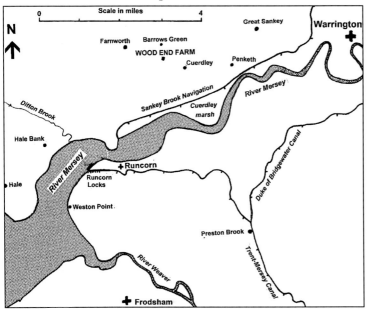

Map of the area near Runcorn in the canal-building era, showing the position of Wood End Farm, home of the Leather family, in relation to Sankey Brook Navigation.

In the September of 1761 Brindley was surveying an extension to take the canal an additional thirty miles to Liverpool, joining the Mersey at the Hempstones, a little above Runcorn. He continued the survey until January 1762, when he went to London to give evidence on the Bill giving powers for the extension to Runcorn, where it was to descend a series of ten locks to reach river level. The full length was completed in 1765. As W W Tomlinson remarks in his book *North Eastern Railway*, 'public interest in canals rose to fever heat in 1767 when James Brindley completed to the upper part of Runcorn, the second portion of his great work – the Duke of Bridgewater's Canal'.

Now Runcorn, with the ferry crossing, was within walking or riding distance of the Leather's Wood End Farm and, according to family tradition, Brindley took brothers Samuel and George as apprentices. It is likely that the two young men took part in some of Brindley's surveys and in canal building itself, both of the Bridgewater Canal and its extension to Runcorn. They certainly learnt the

Canal basin at the junction of the Bradford Canal with the Leeds Liverpool Canal, Dock Lane Shipley

art of surveying and levelling. It is believed that Brindley, as a friend of the family, was actually staying at Wood End Farm when he was invited to become engineer for the Leeds Liverpool Canal at a salary of £400[2]. That was in May 1770 though he declined the post and Longbottom was appointed.

Some time later that year, the Leather brothers Samuel and George, now aged 26 and 23, moved from Merseyside to West Yorkshire. Having received a sound apprenticeship, they were well equipped for surveying and canal engineering, and went initially to Shipley, where Samuel settled. Both he and George may have worked on the three-mile Bradford Canal, from the centre of Bradford to Shipley, surveyed 1770-71, and for which Brindley was engineer. They also probably worked on the Leeds-Liverpool Canal, which runs alongside the River Aire near to Shipley and connects with the Bradford Canal. It was in 1771 that Samuel married Mary Hammerton of Keighley.

George Leather senior – later career George Leather extended his interests to coalmining in the Bradford area where at that time there were many small mines scattered throughout the district. About 1774 George Leather went to work for Thomas Fenton near Wakefield where he became surveyor and engineer in charge of coalmines. According to John Goodchild in his *Coal Kings of Yorkshire*, George Leather was responsible for opening up new works at Rothwell Haigh, Wakefield Outwood, Lofthouse, and Methley and at New Park, all large and important collieries.

At Rothwell Haigh he devised a 'water machine', a mechanism that lowered water down one shaft providing power enough to raise coal up an adjacent one. At New Park colliery near Ossett, George Leather built a great pumping wheel to take water out of the mine. Here he was also responsible for building two dams that provided power for the water wheels he installed. He surveyed and built many colliery railways, both underground and on the surface and, by about 1790, was the first to introduce flanged iron rails or tramplates in the pits[3], replacing simple wooden rails. He built Fenton's Outwood Railway, which ran from Stanley Ferry to Lofthouse Gate, passing through Victoria Colliery. In 1825 his son, George Leather junior stated in his *Evidence to the Liverpool and Manchester Railway Bill*: 'My father was employed in all the railways so long as he lived'. Besides building colliery railways in West Yorkshire George Leather senior was resident engineer for the eight mile Surrey Iron Railway that ran from Croydon to Wandsworth (1801-1805), under Jessop. George Leather senior continued to work for the Fentons, the 'Coal Kings of Yorkshire' until about 1811 – more than thirty-seven years.

---

[2] Notebook belonged to descendant Ernest Leather
[3] George Leather may have been the first to introduce tramplates worldwide.

James Leather (1779-1849)   James was the eldest son of George Leather senior. The second son, George Leather junior, born in 1786, became an eminent civil engineer and James and George grew up amid the opening of new collieries, the laying out of railroads, and the setting up of pumping mechanisms and ventilating systems for coalmines. James lived with his eight younger brothers and sisters, first, until he was ten years old, at Lake Lock, Stanley on the banks of the River Calder and then a mile or so up the hill at Lofthouse Gate, in the Outwood district of north Wakefield. The Leather home at Lofthouse Gate was only a couple of miles from the Towlerton's farmhouse at Kirkhamgate, where James Leather met Mary Towlerton and the two were married when James was twenty-four.

Before his marriage, James wanted to be independent and make his own way in life. He had a good head for figures and, while business was good, he could easily find a job. He had learnt about the coal industry in Yorkshire and also knew about the city of Liverpool from his father who had grown up only ten miles away. The great port was expanding rapidly and coal was a major export, pouring into Liverpool along the new canals. James became an accountant in Liverpool, probably to a local coal-dealing firm. He was living there when he made an application to Wakefield for his marriage licence.

The vicar of Wakefield married James Leather and Mary Towlerton on 15 June 1803 and James took his new wife back to live in Liverpool. Just over a year later on 30 August 1804 in a house in Brook Street in the centre of the city, Mary Leather gave birth to her first child. They decided to name the boy John, after Mary's father, with Mary's maiden name – the unusual one of Towlerton – added as a second Christian name. This was all very traditional and five week old John Towlerton Leather was baptised on 7th October at St Paul's Church Liverpool, just two blocks from where they lived. Brook Street opens out on to the waterfront overlooking Princes Dock and the River Mersey, close to the terminus of the Leeds-Liverpool Canal with in those days a succession of large coal wharves.

James stayed on in Liverpool for several years and in January 1811 a son George was born. Not to be confused with his more famous uncle or his grandfather, this George was to become a colliery viewer in Bradford, a railway contractor at Chesterfield, and a potter in Holbeck. He married Maria Jane Wardle[4], daughter of the vicar of Beeston, and died in India in 1860 –building railways there. This George reached fame in the family by being struck by lightning while out shooting, and surviving to tell the tale.

Later in the year 1811, James and his family moved from Liverpool back to Yorkshire and James took the job of bookkeeper at Beeston Park Colliery. Beeston, situated

---

[4] The name Wardle later became famous in locomotive building near Leeds

two miles south of Leeds, was 'a well-built village on a commanding eminence' with a population of 2,000 inhabitants. The colliery, in the area known as Beeston Park, was away from the village off the Dewsbury road and in a pleasant rural area, backed by Middleton Woods. It was owned by Beeston landowners: Denison, Hill, Walton and Spearman, the last three, being joint lords of the manor of Beeston-cum-Churwell. The old Gothic church in Beeston was a Chapel of Ease, where the Rev Joseph Wardle, MA was incumbent.

Middleton Colliery Railway approaching Brandling's coal staiths on the River Aire, Hunslet Leeds, with Christchurch and warehouses of the Aire Calder Navigation in the background. (photo of engraving Leeds Library and Information Service)

James occupied a house at the colliery and concerned himself with the accounts, paying the miners and increasing his knowledge of colliery management. His son John Towlerton was a boy of six or seven when they moved to Beeston Park where, less than half a mile from their home, there was a horse tramway that ran behind Middleton Woods along the six-mile track bringing coal from the pits at Middleton to Waterloo Staithes alongside the River Aire. The Brandling brothers owned Middleton Colliery and John Blenkinsop was their agent. In 1811, Blenkinsop brilliantly adapted Richard Trevithick's 1802 high pressure steam engine to build a railway locomotive for the colliery tramway that ran from Middleton to Leeds.

Realising that the weight of a locomotive built to Trevithick's design would be too heavy for the brittle cast iron rails of the time, he successfully combined a lighter steam engine with rack propulsion. Blenkinsop sought the help of Matthew Murray who had already built a Trevithick steam engine for use in a paddleboat. So, at the famous Round Foundry at Holbeck, Leeds, the Blenkinsop-Murray locomotive was built.

On 24 June 1812 the new steam locomotive was tried for the first time and was an outstanding success. The engine was able to pull 94 tons on the level at 3½ miles an hour, outstripping all other modes of transport, and it later ran up to ten mph. It was the first commercial steam railway in the world. Not only was it the first steam railway, but also Murray's locomotive was the first to be built in Leeds – the beginning of a very large and important locomotive-building industry.

The eight-year-old John Towlerton Leather may have witnessed the opening of this amazing new form of transport passing just a few hundred yards from his home, and would have seen it regularly over the years as it puffed away hauling the coals from the Middleton pit for market in Leeds. Some fifty years later he himself would become involved in the building of steam locomotives and the founding of the great Hunslet Engine Company.

In the spring of 1813 James' father George Leather senior, the old mine engineer now 65 years old, took a lease on the same Beeston Park Colliery at which James was bookkeeper. So George, along with the help of his two sons James and George junior, took over the running of the colliery at the hefty rent of £2,000 per annum. The colliery had a farm attached and consisted of 'a house, a counting house, nine cottages, a stable, mistal, workshops and engines'.

The coal seams here were thick and lucrative. The Beeston Coal was nine feet thick at Hunslet, and at Beeston, where it divided into two the main seam was still a very valuable eight feet thick. It was a good investment and would produce coal of a high quality for many years to come – and there was a wealth of experience among the three new lessees. As George senior approached seventy, he died at his home at Beeston Park and a short notice appeared in Wright's *Leeds Intelligencer* for Monday 23 February 1818. Not the custom to give detailed obituaries in those days: under 'Deaths' it simply read: 'Saturday week, Mr Leather, of Beeston Park Colliery, near this town.'

In the autumn of 1814, James and Mary Leather had a daughter, Anne Eliza. She became known as Liz and, later, was to make a good marriage to engineer Charles Wetherell Wardle, son of the vicar of Beeston and brother of Maria Jane. Charles Wardle was first of 'Leather and Wardle' pottery makers and then as 'Manning Wardle' a business which became a major locomotive-building company in south Leeds.

John Towlerton Leather (1804-1885)   During much of this time James' eldest son, John Towlerton, was probably sent away to Durham School, though there is no solid evidence and early records of the school have not survived. His cousin John Wignall Leather and brother George certainly did go there. The following could have some bearing on the matter. R S Surtees, the writer of popular Victorian hunting novels, did attend Durham School, and was only few months older than J T Leather. Two of the main characters in *Mr Sponge's Sporting Tour* (1853) are Peter Leather and Tom Towler, the one a rogue and the other ugly. 'Tom Towler' is only one letter different from 'Towler-ton'. Later in life John Towlerton Leather wrote a number of letters to his grandson, but never referred to his own school days. Being of a rather quiet disposition, it is possible he was picked on or bullied at school, resulting in unhappy childhood memories that he never wanted to talk about.

J T Leather had a brother Charles James Leather who later become a contractor in his own right in Portsmouth when JTL was engaged on the extension of Portsmouth Dockyard. Charles James Leather married Charlotte Ann Wardle. The links between the Leathers and the Wardles became ever tighter.

In 1823, John Towlerton Leather was seventeen years old. He had shown great promise with a particular gift for mathematics and it is thought that he attended Edinburgh University, a centre noted for engineers and where mathematics was strong. According to family tradition, he gained a gold medal in the subject. In those days engineers did not generally go to university, to be immersed in the Classics, but began their profession on the job and, preferably apprenticed to an eminent engineer. In fact, JTL gained his knowledge of surveying and colliery management from his father and continued an apprenticeship with his uncle, George Leather junior, with whom he 'served his articles'.

John Towlerton Leather now had a certain presence and authority, though generally he was quiet and reserved. He was so thin, he used to say, that his fellow students called him 'Euclid's definition of a line' – length without breadth or thickness. When JTL was nineteen he decided to leave home with five pounds in his pocket. He later recalls the occasion on his eightieth birthday in a letter to his grandson:

> *"No doubt, at first, the task was a hard one, for I left my father's house before I was twenty and I never troubled him again in any way: he gave me £5 and said goodbye, and I went my way into the world with a firm determination never to place myself under obligations to any man, if I could possibly avoid it. I had then three brothers and a sister – all much younger than myself – and I felt that I ought to set the example of leaving home in order to make room for the juniors, and I hardly need say that I have never had cause to regret that step."*

This marks the beginning of three years' apprenticeship (1823-26) with uncle George Leather junior, who was making a name for himself as an outstanding civil engineer.

In 1820 George Leather was appointed consulting engineer to the Aire and Calder Navigation. This work included surveying of the proposed canal from Knottingley to Goole, and the design and construction at Goole of two three-acre docks, one for ships and the other for barges. The Thwaite and Leeds locks on the River Aire were being rebuilt and a new lock and flood lock at Knostrop was constructed. By 1825 the Cryer Cut Flood Lock had been widened to eighteen feet, the new standard width. In 1824, George Leather also surveyed the routes of two railways, one in county Durham and the other in

River Aire viewed from Leeds Bridge near the beginning of the Aire Calder Navigation. (photo Leeds Library and Information Service)

Monk Bridge over the River Aire Leeds at Whitehall Road, built in 1827 and designed by George Leather jnr. This is the first example in Western Europe of a bridge built with rigid arch and suspended roadway. (photo Leeds Library and Information Service)

West Yorkshire. In addition to canal works and surveys for railways, George Leather became responsible for the design of several cast iron bridges, including the Monk, Astley and Hunslet Bridges over the River Aire. Monk Bridge, built in 1827 to carry the Halifax road into Leeds, was the first built in Western Europe and possibly the first in the world to make use of the rigid arch and suspended roadway (like the Sydney Harbour bridge). 1825-26 also saw the enlargement by George Leather of the Worsborough reservoir, which served the Dove and Dearne Canal.

There was thus a considerable amount and variety of work in progress in George Leather's office which, until 1825, was in High Street, Bradford (just above the parish church and near Paper Hall) where he lived with his family. His eldest daughter, Maria – later John Towlerton Leather's first wife – was in her early teens while his son, John Wignall, was at Durham School. For JTL it was a period of intense work that probably included a ten-hour day or more. In the office he would be copying drawings, sections and plans – learning his craft from 'one of the most outstanding engineers in the country'[5]. Outdoors he travelled to various parts of the county surveying, levelling and visiting sites where canals, locks, bridges and reservoirs were in the course of construction. The most expensive piece of equipment he would carry with him was a theodolite and tripod, and he would probably have pocket sextant, level, plumb line and measuring equipment. The surveying of the route of a proposed railway could be a tricky business, especially when a landowner took strong objection to a line passing over his land. The surveyor could come up against physical force and would have to be on the alert to dodge any of the landowner's men who might confront him. JTL was obtaining a wide practical experience of his chosen career.

In 1825, George Leather and family moved into Leeds, to a house on Park Terrace on the Headrow, close to the city centre where George had offices, conveniently placed for his projects along the River Aire and throughout West Yorkshire.

A year later the heads of the two Leather families, the two brothers James and George, became full joint colliery owners (rather than lessees) when they purchased the Beeston Park colliery outright. There was still a lot of potential in the coalmine with that eight-foot thick coal seam. They owned the colliery for ten years until 1835 when it was sold[6], James keeping the farm and land, managing it until his death in 1849.

In 1826, John Towlerton Leather left his uncle's office in Leeds to help build up the Beeston Park colliery business which was in need of some attention. At this time his uncle writes of him '*he seems tolerably industrious and I hope he will do some good.*'

[5] G M Binnie FRS, former President of the Newcomen Society
[6] to Thomas Taylor, Benjamin Burnley and Tottenham Lee.

To summarise the three generations of engineers, the first was George Leather senior, colliery engineer to Yorkshire Coal Kings, Thomas and William Fenton. In addition to the collieries and railroads, George senior worked on navigation improvements to the River Don (1808) for William Jessop and the construction of the Derwent Navigation (c1810). He was also resident engineer under William Jessop for the construction of the Surrey Iron Railway in 1805. The outstanding engineer of the next generation was George Leather junior[7]. In building the Surrey Iron Railway, George junior undertook some of the work for his father. He also took on the construction of the Pocklington Canal after his father declined, and in 1820 was appointed engineer to the Aire and Calder Navigation. Between 1822 and 1838 George Leather junior was engineer to Goole Docks and the town of Goole. He designed and built four major cast iron bridges, was engineer to the Stockton and Hartlepool Railway, the Birmingham and Derby Junction Railway and the Holme reservoirs near Huddersfield. The third generation was John Towlerton Leather, grandson of George senior and the subject of this biography, and the next we hear of him is in 1829 when, at the age of twenty-five, he decided to set up his own business in Sheffield

---

[7] For further details of the engineering achievements of both George Leather senior and George Leather junior see entries in *The Biographical Dictionary of Civil Engineers* (Thomas Telford, 2002).

Sheffield's Water Engineer

In the early summer of 1829, twenty-four year old John Towlerton Leather was at his family home at Beeston Park, south of Leeds. He had busied himself over the last three years running and sorting out the colliery of which the Leather family was now sole owner and he now found himself at a loose end. He was musing on his comfortless life and generally feeling sorry for himself, when suddenly he made the decision to 'seek his fortune'. He got up very early one morning and caught the 5 o'clock stagecoach to Sheffield. He spent the whole day in the town making enquiries and returned home next day. He told his father he had made up his mind to open an office and set up business in Sheffield as a civil engineer and surveyor. His father James was delighted and wholeheartedly supported the new venture, offering useful financial assistance to get him going. JTL was so astonished by his father's response that, as he wrote in a letter to his friend Captain Mervyn Richardson in Bristol[8]:

> 'I did not run and catch him by the neck, neither did I fall down on my knees to thank him, but it was with the utmost difficulty I restrained myself from leaping across the table at him. However I did manage to express the gratitude I felt in a plain straight-forward way, for at the best I am but a poor stick at this work. I am like the rest of my species I suppose, I can do these things better by deeds than words. But when I came a little to my senses I began to fear that this was but a temporary fit of kindness, yet I am glad to say that it has lasted better than I expected, not that I can in my heart attribute it all to paternal affection, else it would have been a little more substantial. I think there has been a little of such a feeling as 'I shall thus be rid of him', not very flattering to me; nevertheless here I am, as large as life, writing to my friend Mr R in my own offices where I hope to practice the profession of Civil Engineer, Land and Mineral Surveyor etc. etc., in all their varied branches, that is when I can get anything to do, for at present I am

---

[8] This letter was undelivered in Bristol and returned to the sender. It is known that Captain Mervyn Richardson married about this time and in 1845 had two sons who attended King William's College, Castletown, Isle of Man where the family lived.

doing nothing from the reason, they tell me, of my not being sufficiently known. This hindrance, however, I am trying with all my power to set aside by means of introductions, circulars etc., so that I trust I shall not long have to grumble about this, and what is no less surprising to me is, the truly generous manner in which my Uncle [George Leather] has put his shoulder to the wheel. He has introduced me to many of the first people in the neighbourhood, given me every information and promises more...

I have got lodgings at about a mile from my offices in a most delightful situation and where the old lady and her good man (the whole of the family) are independent of the world and consequently very nice to whom they let their rooms. When I first called upon her she asked me some such questions as are you an officer? a rake? or extravagant? and upon certifying that I was none of them, she consented to take me, and so far as I can yet able to judge, I shall be extremely comfortable. She nurses me as if I was her own bairn. But I am running on to a great length all about myself...'

John Towlerton Leather chose Sheffield to set up on his own. For four years his uncle George had been based in Leeds so, to be completely independent as a civil engineer, he would go elsewhere. He would include 'mineral surveying' in his professional description. He knew the local coal measure geology – just where and how thick the seams of coal and ironstone were. He had no doubt heard public lectures in Leeds or Sheffield by William Smith, the canal builder now living in Yorkshire, who had made a geological map of Yorkshire, showing the commercial deposits of coal, building stone, limestone, fireclay and so on. By his 'Natural Order of Strata', William Smith had produced a key to scientific prospecting, essential knowledge for mineral surveying and a valuable basis for civil engineering projects.

JTL must also have thought carefully about his departure from Beeston Park and made an intelligent decision. He was a bright young man with a promising future, and he wanted to be successful in his main ambition. He had valuable practical experience and a clear vision of his next move. He set up offices in Castle Street in the centre of Sheffield where the old-established city was booming. It was close to the fish market, the fruit market and the hay market and may not have been ideal, but nonetheless very central. Until now JTL had been known as John within the family, but to differentiate himself from his uncle John Leather, who was already in Sheffield as an architect and surveyor, and to promote himself in his business, he now signed himself J Towlerton Leather, as he did for the rest of his life. He appreciated the attractive countryside round the city, though he did voice misgivings the wet weather in the hills above Sheffield.

Based upon crucible steel, Sheffield had always specialised in the manufacture of cutting tools such as knives, saws and files, and was known throughout the world for its quality household cutlery. The sandstone of the area was excellent for grinding and sharpening and the local streams provided much needed water-power. The city nestles on the eastern slopes of the Pennine moors, at a point where four small rivers – the Sheaf, the Porter, the Rivelin and the Loxley which run in deep valleys – converge to form the River Don. Sheffield is named after the River Sheaf.

Sheffield was expanding fast industrially and by 1830 the population had reached 90,000, having doubled in the previous thirty years. The supply of water to the town was an attractive proposition for speculators, and rival schemes including supplies from the River Sheaf and from springs to the northwest of the town were on the cards. In response, the owners of the existing Sheffield Water Company applied for an Act of Parliament to enable them to construct large service and compensation reservoirs on a much bigger scale than anything previously contemplated. The competition faded and the result was the 1830 Act and a brand new water company.

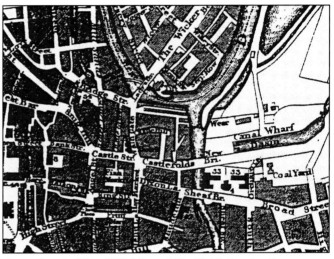

A small part of the 1823 'Plan of Sheffield' showing the city centre and the position of Castle Street. Surveyed by John Leather uncle of J T Leather.

It was then that our budding engineer was appointed to the newly formed Sheffield Waterworks Company, at a salary of £300 a year (add two noughts for a modern equivalent). He was to be their first Managing Clerk, Resident Engineer and Surveyor[9]. By the following April (of 1831) he was made First Engineer with superintendence of all water works. He remained consulting engineer to the Sheffield Waterworks until 1865 – a period of thirty-four years.

He began immediately with the building of two reservoirs. The first was the Redmires embankment (later known as Middle Redmires), in the hills about five miles west of the city, on Wyming Brook, a small tributary of the Rivelin. From Redmires a 4½ mile watercourse was to lead to Crooks Moor, where the second reservoir, the Hadfield, was constructed.

[9] *Early Victorian Water Engineers* by G M Binnie (Thomas Telford, 1981).

At Crooks Moor the Sheffield Waterworks had its headquarters. Here the Hadfield Reservoir stands high above the city with an area of five and a half acres. According to William Terry, formerly General Manager of Sheffield Corporation Waterworks Department, in his *"History and Description of the Sheffield Waterworks"* (1908), when excavating at Crooks Moor, some old coal workings were discovered, together with mining tools of which there was no existing record. To prevent water from leaking through the workings, the bottom of the reservoir had to be puddled. The work was completed in 1833 and the enthusiastic company's annual report stated:

> 'The new Reservoir at Crooks is now also ready for use... The substantial manner in which the work has been executed, under the direction of Mr J T Leather, the Company's engineer, will, it is hoped, meet with the approval of the Proprietors – the Masonry of the Feed pit, and the Tunnel for carrying off the waste or surplus Water, are especially worthy of attention.'

The Middle Redmires was initially a compensation reservoir and at a later date became a storage reservoir for the town's water supply. It was finished in three years with a dam height of forty-nine feet, and length of 750 yards along the crest. The outlet consisted of a twelve-inch diameter cast iron standpipe at the upstream toe of the embankment, with two controlled inlets at different levels. The inlets were coupled to a twelve-inch diameter cast-iron pipeline that ran through a stone-lined tunnel four feet in diameter under the embankment. The watertight puddle clay core was eight feet thick at the base, narrowing to four feet at the top. The tunnel

Middle Redmires Reservoir, set out in 1836 and superintended by John Fowler when apprenticed as a young engineer to J T Leather.

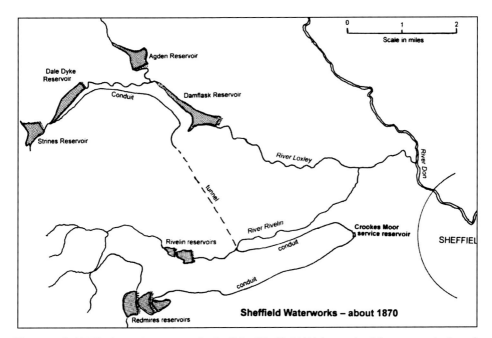

The map (c1870) shows ten reservoirs built by Sheffield Waterworks. They were designed by Chief Engineer J Towlerton Leather except Strines and Damflask which though planned by JTL were designed and built by Thomas Hawksley and completed in 1871 and 1896.

also had a jacket of puddle clay. These details are given in view of what was to occur later.

In 1836 the Management Committee, referring to the progress on Redmires, wrote that the excavation and embankment were nearly completed. Provision was made to increase the capacity of the reservoir, and this was carried out a few years later by the construction of a wall along the top of the embankment. This raised the reservoir level by five feet and increased the volume by 50%.

Altogether JTL designed seven dams at Sheffield and all were earth embankments across river valleys with a clay puddle core wall down the middle. Six of them are still in use. Apart from a few modifications, dams of a similar design are still being built today.

From Middle Redmires to Crooks on the borders of Sheffield the conduit or gravity flow waterway, some of it still in existence today, had some vertical drops of several feet, which after heavy rain made attractive waterfalls. A cast iron aqueduct on stone pillars took it thirty feet high over the Tapton valley.

By 1837, twenty-five miles of cast iron water pipes had been laid in the city, half of them replacing wooden pipes, which were not very effective and prone to leaks.

Some wooden pipes were left in the ground, as it was considered too expensive to replace them all. The wooden pipes were made from oak or ash trunks and measured from nine to twelve inches in diameter on the outside. They were bored through the centre with holes from three to six inches across. The pipes were bored by hand and joined by means of a taper at one end and an inner cone at the other. Wool was used as packing to make the joints watertight. Some lasted many years without rotting. However, from about 1830, iron pipes became the norm.

William Terry describes how the people in Sheffield had a prejudice against the 'Company's water' brought to each house at so much a year. The job of the water carrier was in danger, and many of the old folk continued in the traditional way of buying a pailful or two for a penny. 'Oh dear', they said, 'what's the world coming to? They won't let poor folks live. And they're breaking up the roads again, and we shall be under water some day with their new-fangled goings on!'

Portrait of Sir John Fowler in his later years

In 1833 – when the Hadfield and Redmires reservoirs were being constructed – a sixteen-year-old from Sheffield by the name of John Fowler persuaded his father to let him be apprenticed to Mr J T Leather. John Fowler[10], who later was to become 'Sir John Fowler' and President of the Institution of Civil Engineers, was born in Sheffield in 1817. He was the eldest of a large family and after a school education at Whitley Hall in Sheffield, he decided on his chosen profession and elected to gain practical knowledge and experience under the guidance of John Towlerton Leather. Later in life Sir John Fowler in some autobiographical notes wrote:

'This was fortunate for my future career, as I had a thorough training in waterworks engineering, and set out and superintended the Redmires and Crooks reservoirs of the company and all the business of pipe testing and pipe laying in every detail'. During my pupilage I was frequently at Leeds with

---

[10] Obituary of Sir John Fowler in *Minutes of Proceedings of the Institution of Civil Engineers* Vol. 135 (1898-99), p328, and *The Life of John Fowler* by Thomas Mackay (John Murray, 1900).

Mr Leather's uncle, who was engineer of the Great Aire and Calder Navigation, Goole Docks etc., to give him assistance when he was much pressed by professional work. The result being that my early training was exclusively waterworks and hydraulic engineering; and before I was nineteen I was a good engineering surveyor and leveller, could set out works, and measure them up for certificates to be paid to contractors.'

John Fowler's apprenticeship lasted five years. In 1834 he was in George Leather's Leeds office copying the specification for the 'immense ship lock at Goole – the largest in the world – and other locks, bridges and three miles of canal for the Aire and Calder Navigation, at a cost of about £100,000'. In 1836 he was sent to Birmingham to survey a possible Birmingham to Gloucester railway line for George Leather. By July 1837, with Leather testimonials, he applied for a job with the North Midland line, and by the beginning of 1838 was established first in Birmingham then London. In August 1839 John Fowler wrote one of many letters to his father:

'On Wednesday last I received a letter from Mr J T Leather, stating that his uncle [George Leather] was in want of someone to be on a railway of his in Durham, and wishing me either to come or write immediately on the subject.

I consequently left London on Thursday night, as I conceived writing would be a very imperfect mode of obtaining proper and correct information of the nature of the situation, salary, etc, and it appeared it was necessary to be decided in the shortest possible time.

On my arrival in Leeds, and calling on Mr Leather, I found the situation he wished me to take as follows:

To be at Seaton, in Durham, on the railway, and his office in Leeds alternately, and the salary he could give £200 a year.

Now as this is something different to what you expected me to do, and, in fact, what I intended to do myself, I will detail to you the circumstances which influenced me in deciding on the step I have taken, which is to accept the appointment.

Mr Leather's office is a most excellent one (from the varied and miscellaneous work presented) for improvement, and some of a character with which in a great measure I am unacquainted, and the railway in Durham has sea embanking and other peculiar works which make it desirable, and I am desirous of getting yet more information on works. And generally there are several things which will be better obtained in his office than anywhere else, before I commence business on my own account; and in future I am convinced the only way for a man to be successful is to understand all the scientific and practical part of engineering well.

I certainly only propose to remain a year with Mr Leather, and intend to open offices in Sheffield on the 1ˢᵗ of September, 1840, but this is not what I should like Mr Leather to know, as he might not perhaps be pleased...'

John Fowler took the job of resident engineer to the Hartlepool and Stockton railway and then as engineer for Hartlepool docks. By the time he was twenty-six he was working independently on railways across the country. His greatest works were the railway tunnels built in the 1860s under the streets of London – the London Underground – linking the main line stations and admired as a great feat of engineering. In the 1880s, his masterpiece was the magnificent Forth Bridge, carrying the railway across the Firth of Forth on its way north from Edinburgh. Although he worked for George Leather as much as for John Towlerton, he always looked back at his time with JTL as a happy one. In a letter to his father, John Fowler wrote of the kindliness of John Towlerton Leather adding that he looked upon him as a second father – *a pater secundus*.

Sir John Fowler's brother, Henry Fowler also trained in the office of John Towlerton Leather from September 1838 for a period of one year. After working in India Henry Fowler returned to England and died young soon afterwards.

JTL had admired his cousin Maria, eldest daughter of his uncle George, for many years. She was seven years younger than he, and had grown into a very attractive young lady. She was slim and had a serious-looking oval face with the long straight nose, a sensual, pursed mouth and long dark hair, done up in a bun. However, Maria's father was very much against a match between them and JTL wrote about this in the letter to Mervyn Richardson in 1829:

'...he [uncle George Leather] is always so violent against my connection with Maria, not that he ever mentioned such a thing to me, nor I to him, strange as it may appear, but my reason for not doing so were the vileness of my prospects in the world... There he has... [letter torn] famously telling them [Maria and her mother] that he would never consent to it, for I was all that was bad and so on. But after all this, why should he here give me almost the best of characters? This is what puzzles me, because if I was in his place and found a youth paying attention to my daughter whom I did not approve, I should tell him so at once, and if he resisted, should without further ceremony kick him out of my door, but certainly not without a sufficient reason. Surely there must be something to hope for at the bottom of all this? In fact

it was partly from these considerations that I was prevented adopting the desperate alternative named in your last, but don't you think if I succeed here that I am taking the wisest plan of the two? Because he is rather of a stern, determined character, and when he once implies a prejudice, he does not easily rid himself of it.'

JTL did not seem to realise that his uncle was fundamentally opposed to the marriage simply because they were first cousins. George Leather had revealed his strong opinions five years earlier to his seventeen-year-old son John Wignall, who was having a crush on *his* cousin Eliza, who was in love with *her* cousin Charles. The following extract is from a letter to John Wignall Leather at Durham School:

George Leather junior, J Towlerton Leather's uncle and father of Maria Leather, JTL's first cousin and sweetheart. From the scowl on his face, not a person you would wish to cross.

'*My Dear Boy your mother as well as every one else who is not wilfully blind can readily discover the real cause of Eliza's pains, it is not to the powers of medicines they are likely to give way, her mind is affected; she is fostering a foolish passion for her Cousin Charles… It is notorious to all her friends, and she herself makes a boast of being in love with her Cousin Charles, and she frequently broods over this while she makes herself ill – and her fainting fits are to be attributed to this cause more than any other – for my own part I always consider a connection between cousins as almost criminal. It is next to a connection between Brother and Sister, and the notion because first cousins are not forbidden to marry by the Common Laws therefore it is proper, is most absurd and cannot bear a moment's reflection; and so satisfied are some of the greatest men of the present day of the impropriety of such connection that a Bill was brought into Parliament a session or two ago to make marriages between cousins unlawful, it did not however pass at that time, but it is probable it may do so in some future session. – I fear from the feeling with which you speak of Eliza you are a little struck with her, but I can scarcely suspect you of such a round of manly feelings so as to be harkening after a woman, even were there no other objections, who makes a boast of being in love with another, besides My Dear Boy at your age to harbour feelings of this sort at all is to say the least of it extreme folly.'*

During the summer of 1832 there must have been many clandestine meetings, love letters written, messages delivered and a huge decision to be made – was it one of the heart or the head? JTL had a highly responsible job at Sheffield Waterworks and his prospects had changed dramatically, but still his uncle was unchanging in his belief that a cousin should not marry a cousin. However, John Towlerton was adamant, and Maria must have had just as much a say in the matter. They would make a stolen match as soon as Maria reached twenty-one and was legally of age. On the second day of August, her birthday, dressed in her finest riding habit of green cloth, and a top hat placed on her head fastened with ribbons, Maria rode on horseback along the Headrow in Leeds from her home on Park Terrace to St Peter's Church. The church was the old medieval parish church which five years later was pulled down and rebuilt. JTL led his trusting and beautiful bride down Briggate turning left along Kirkgate, all the way to the altar. It was the first marriage of the day and the vicar himself, the Rev Richard Fawcett, took the service. John was nearly twenty-eight. He had obtained a licence the previous day from the vicar, thus avoiding the publicity and a wait of three weeks for the banns. It might have been one of the big weddings of the year but, as it was, there could not have been many guests on this occasion. Against the odds, JTL had successfully pulled it off and taken the prize. This was a formula

Exterior of Leeds Parish Church in 1838 just before this old St Peter's was pulled down and rebuilt. (Leeds Library and Information Service)

he was to repeat many times in his life.

On her wedding day Maria was already pregnant, and their daughter Emily was born in Sheffield before the end of the year. The green riding habit was kept in the family, though on the day of the wedding there may have been adjustments to make to it. Years later it was said that the waist of the dress was so slim that it never fitted any of Maria's daughters. This was a neat cover-up regarding the

Interior of Leeds Parish Church where John Towlerton Leather and Maria Leather were married and where they owned a pew – from a painting made in 1838 (Leeds Library and Information Service)

pregnancy, but sadly, little Emily lived for only seven months, and was buried in Beeston churchyard by their family friend the Reverend Joseph Wardle. The late summer of 1832 was a terrible time in Sheffield when cholera struck and, of over 1,000 people who contracted the disease, about 500 perished. Many kept away from the city. In fact the wedding in Leeds was at about the height of the epidemic.

What was the reaction of George Leather to having his daughter made pregnant and snatched from under his eyes on her twenty-first birthday? There is no record but George must have been absolutely furious. His photograph taken later in life shows an enraged expression that looks fairly permanent. But this was his eldest and favourite daughter and his nephew was advancing very well as a civil engineer under his guidance. He couldn't cast them off never to speak to them again, so he had to tolerate the situation. He must have confronted John Towlerton but then may have subdued his anger and kept quiet on the subject, while endeavouring to further the couple's comfort and happiness. It was a period in history when there was a campaign against the union of first cousins. Opposition has still persisted especially in the western world, though one of the best known examples was Charles Darwin's marriage to his first cousin Emma Wedgwood in 1839. The couple had ten healthy children and Darwin doubted that such consanguineous relationships led to defects

Maria Leather, first wife of John Towlerton Leather and daughter of George Leather jnr with daughter Ellen (born 1838). The drawing is from a painting, now lost.

in the offspring. Recent research has shown him to be correct[11]. However, as far as the two Leather families were concerned, there remained a substantial bond between them and plenty of communication too, at both social and business level.

On 16 July 1834, John Towlerton and Maria had a second daughter, Ellen Eliza. But although their home was in Sheffield the baby was born at Beeston Park, her father-in-law's home. One reason Maria preferred Beeston might have been the presence of cholera in both Sheffield and Leeds. Ellen Eliza appears on the portrait with Maria – a neat pencil drawing. She lived on to be eighty years old. In November

1835, the third child, Frederick John was born, their first son, who lived to inherit his father's estate. So within three years of their wedding, Maria had had three babies. There was a pause of four years before the next.

John Towlerton Leather aged 49. (detail from colour portrait)

[11] Motulsky and Bennett, University of Washington in *The Journal of Genetic Counselling*, April 2002.

By 1834 John Towlerton Leather was listed in Pigot's National and Commercial Directory as 'Civil Engineer, Manager of Waterworks, Division Street, Sheffield'. He was soon to branch out and establish himself as both consultant *and contractor*. He was becoming known, and work came in from a wide area: surveying, pricing, acting as referee, and problem solving. His consultancy work brought in useful additional income, which he would need if he were to set up as a contractor. He was extremely astute where money was concerned, investing wisely and wasting little. He never borrowed a penny.

Railway Contractor and Colliery Manager

The nineteenth century contractor was a rare breed, a combination of entrepreneur, designer, civil engineer and active genius who could see the job through. Contracting entailed using costly machinery such as steam locomotives, wagons, cranes, and the employment and payment of hundreds of navvies. Huge amounts of earth, rock, stone and debris had to be removed and transported. Wagonways had to be built, stone quarries opened up, temporary scaffolding and piers erected, excavations made and embankments constructed. Every situation was unique: new and often complicated construction methods were invented for each contest between man and nature.

The contractor first had to put in a tender for the job. The whole contract had to be researched and priced in the sure knowledge that it could be carried out for the amount agreed, and within the time specified. Complex constructions such as tunnels, bridges and viaducts had to be scrutinised in detail and costed accurately. There was stiff competition between contractors: directors and their shareholders usually went for the cheapest, regardless of the differing quality of the finished work.

The contractor initially received part payment, with the major balance due when the job was completed. Not only did he need financial backing before setting out on a large contract, but also had to own the tools, equipment, machinery and plant used in the work. The contract could take several months or even years, and there would always be problems that might delay completion. The successful nineteenth century civil engineer/contractor was a highly confident man who had an up-to-date working knowledge of all the relevant sciences: geology, mineral resources, hydrology, strength of materials, metallurgy, mathematics, levelling, map making and so on. He possessed confidence needed to tame, control and dominate the landscape. Such a person was John Towlerton Leather and there were few that matched him.

Early in 1836 JTL was elected Associate Member of the Institution of Civil Engineers. On his application form he is described as Resident Engineer to the Sheffield Waterworks. The three signatories included John MacNeill, the Scottish railway builder who later became Sir John MacNeill – the other two were George Lowe and Joshua Field. JTL was content to remain an Associate until much later in

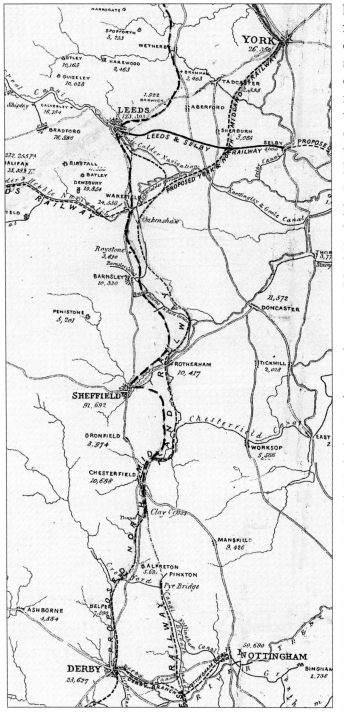

life when at the age of seventy-five he became a full Member of the Institution, with a string of famous signatories on his application form. He rarely attended meetings of the Institution, and made no contributions to the Transactions, though he must have personally known many of the contributors and engineers of the day.

In his need for capital for the acquisition of plant and machinery for the contracting business, he was fortunate. In 1835, the family-owned colliery at Beeston Park was put up for sale releasing a considerable sum of money for further use within the family and this came at just the right time for JTL.

John Towlerton's young apprentice, John Fowler, who had worked on Sheffield's waterworks was seconded to work in his uncle's office in Leeds where George Leather was surveying a proposed Midland Counties Railway, in competition with George Stephenson's North Midland

George Leather versus George Stephenson. Part of the map of the two railway routes proposed by these two gentlemen which came before Parliament in 1836, showing Leather's line calling in at both Sheffield and Leeds, but missing York. (map Leeds Library and Information Service)

Railway. It was to go before Parliament in the 1836 session. Both lines called in at Chesterfield, while George Leather's route then called in at both Sheffield and Leeds, but bypassed York. The Stephenson plan was drawn up to avoid the steep gradients of a line to Sheffield and took the gentle gradients to York. Both plans converged again at Northallerton to proceed along the same line north to Darlington. The Stephenson line was preferred and George and Robert Stephenson were appointed engineers at a joint salary of £2000. John Fowler gives a personal description of this 'Leather versus Stephenson' contest.

> *The Stephenson's projected the Midland Railway, and as it was proposed to pass at a distance from Sheffield, the Sheffield people opposed it in Parliament, and employed Mr Leather to represent them, and as a matter of course I was set to work to discover alternative lines to put Sheffield on the main line. But all in vain, Stephenson carried everything before him, and Sheffield was put on a branch.'*

George Stephenson's emphasis on gentle gradients was not all that necessary, but nevertheless the big man won the day. A Line from Rotherham to Sheffield was subsequently built and opened in the autumn of 1838, linking the city with the main line of the North Midland Railway. Neither George Leather nor John Fowler attended the opening and were contemptuous of the tall talk indulged in by George Stephenson and landowner Earl Fitzwilliam. Both Sheffield and the engineers with their alternative lines had been slighted.

However, railways had to be built and J Towlerton Leather was embarking on a contracting career. He teamed up with his younger brother George and in August 1837 put in a tender[12], for the Chesterfield contract of the North Midland Railway, one that he and his brother partnered with John Waring as 'Leather and Waring Co'. John Waring was an experienced contractor, having won the North Wingfield section of the same line earlier in the year. The joint tender was successful on 31 August 1837, at £32,164 and the great man George Stephenson, together with son Robert, were the engineers.

Two years later JTL, again with his brother George, became 'J & G Leather of Chesterfield' for two other contracts on the North Midland Railway. They put in for the Leeds contract at £83,013 (amended to £69,790) but which went finally to Bray and Duckett for £57,632. On the same August day in 1839, the Rothwell contract tendered by JTL for £11,700 went to John Mawson at £10,322-18s. So both of these contracts were lost. In the same period a contract was let to 'J T Leather and G Leather' on a section of the Birmingham and Derby Junction Railway which ran

---

[12] L Popplewell, *A Gazetteer of Railway Contractors of Central England* (Nelledgen Press, 1986)

from Birmingham through Tamworth and Burton upon Trent, to Derby. So although losing two of the contracts he had two valuable ones under his belt.

JTL's younger brother George was beginning a career in the railway construction business and he married Maria Jane Wardle, eldest daughter of the Reverend Joseph Wardle of Beeston. This is the first of three marriage links between the Leather and Wardle families. In 1844 George goes into partnership with Charles Wetherell Wardle (Maria Jane's brother) at Victoria Pottery, Holbeck Moor.

In 1837 Edward Pease Smith was appointed sub-resident engineer for the Chesterfield section. This was the beginning of a long and close relationship between John Towlerton Leather and Edward Pease Smith. The two men worked together on some very large contracts over the next forty years. JTL took a house in Derbyshire in the village of Whittington, not far from Chesterfield, where he stayed with his wife Maria for three and a half years until the spring of 1842. George and Robert Stephenson lived not far away at Tapton House, Tapton, with George Stephenson's wife Elizabeth. The two villages of Tapton and Whittington were within easy reach of the line of the new railway.

There was some urgency in carrying out the Chesterfield contract. Although sealed on the last day of August 1837, work had already started in June, when Waring and Leather replaced a contractor named Bridge. They had to provide a bond of £3216 being ten percent of the contract price, which was to be completed by the first of January 1840. There was so much pressure to get the contract completed in time that in March 1838 fires were lit at night to enable the navvy excavators to work round the clock. By May 1838 there were 142 workmen on the job. These included 76 excavators, 17 masons, 8 millwrights, 6 sawyers, 3 smiths, 11 horse drivers and carters, 15 labourers and 6 foremen.[13] It is possible JTL employed the navvies directly rather than the common procedure of employing them through sub-contractors. He was able to get on with his men and was known to treat them fairly.

The navvies were workmen a cut above the ordinary labourer. Their work was tough, they tended to live on site and move with the railway. They were paid more and, it is said, were happy on two pounds of beef and a gallon of beer a day. They wore moleskin trousers, canvas shirts, tailcoats, hobnailed boots and a colourful neckerchief and waistcoat. Pay came once a month and was spent mainly on beer. Things could become wild at the end of the month and work would not start again for two or three days after pay day. At this time local courts would be kept busy, too.

The railway had to be level or with very gentle gradients. Cuttings were made through higher ground and embankments across hollows. Streams and rivers had

---

[13] Leeds Committee Minutes of the North Midland Railway, PRO, Rail, 530/4

to be bridged, with arched viaducts over longer stretches of lowland, and tunnels constructed through hills. Earth and rock from cuttings could be used further along the line for building up an embankment. And the navvies with pick shovel and barrow, and horses to draw the wagons did it all. A steam engine or steam crane was only occasionally available.

In the village of Whittington the Leathers became acquainted with George and Elizabeth Stephenson at Tapton House, where the great engineer had finally settled although he was often in London or on site attending to his many projects. George Stephenson, inventor in 1825 of *Locomotion No 1* (Stockton and Darlington Railway) and in 1829 of the famous *Rocket* for the Liverpool to Manchester Railway, was perhaps the most famous engineer of all time, and now in his late fifties. His portrait and a picture of the *Rocket* adorned the British five-pound note for several years. JTL and Maria must also have become acquainted with the Spencer Page family who lived a dozen miles to the south at Shirland near Alfreton. Harriet, the eldest daughter of Isaac Spencer Page, Lord of the Manor, was eight years younger than Maria but the two families met socially.

George Stephenson, the Grand Old Man of Railways, a near neighbour of JTL and his Chief Engineer for the Chesterfield Contract.

In the spring of 1839 Maria gave birth to her fourth child, Anne Maria, and two years later in February 1841, Catherine Rosa was born. However, by June of that year, Maria was back in her family home at Knostrop, taking with her the two baby girls. Her father's house, Knostrop New Hall, was a large and spacious gentleman's residence, far more attractive for Maria with young people coming and going all the time, and not far away there were more of the family at Beeston Park – JTL's family home.

On 21 September 1841, JTL's sister Liz and Charles Wetherell Wardle were married in the new St Peters Church, Leeds. For a time the couple lived on at the Leather home. The following April Liz wrote to her sister in law in Sheffield:

Beeston Park, April 2nd, 1842

My dear Maria,
When my dear Charles obtains a situation I know of no other drawback to any Content. And I trust that trouble will soon be relieved... I am happy to say dear Mother and Charles James are both much better. I suppose you will have been very busy all the week removing to Sheffield

- 33 -

(a very pleasant thing I am sure). You will be heartily glad when comfortably settled. You will perhaps not have heard that Bywater[14] the violin player in Leeds, is dead. He died last Tuesday rather suddenly as I understand. Mrs Teale said about an hour previous to his death that he was doing very well and had been improving since Saturday. As William is waiting to go to Leeds I must conclude with all our kind love to yourself, John and the children.

> *And believe me dear Maria.*
>
> *Your affectionate Sister, A E Wardle.*

So in April 1842, JTL and Maria had moved from Whittington in Derbyshire back to Sheffield, to Dam House at Crooks Moor, the headquarters of Sheffield Waterworks, a change that Maria was most happy about. At last she would be more permanently settled and Dam House was the new address. The house was on the west side of the town in pleasant surroundings and less than a mile from the city centre. It was a bit nearer to Knostrop and Beeston Park than Whittington was, but how many people did she know in Sheffield? And what about schooling for the children? She wasn't happy for long. A year later, her father George mentions the possibility of obtaining for her the Manor House at Whitkirk, on the north side of Temple Newsam. But the Whitkirk Manor purchase was dropped, and JTL was fortunate that, later in 1843, Kirkby Fenton vacated Leventhorpe Hall and agreed to sell it.

Colliery Manager at Leventhorpe Hall Moving up in the world is a constant theme throughout JTL's life and his next home was very grand indeed, being of

Leventhorpe Hall, designed by John Carr of York, became the home of J T Leather in 1844. It is seen here complete with the two wings which were dismantled in the twentieth century.

[14] Leader of the Leeds Promenade Concert Orchestra

the stately variety. Fortune seemed to fall into his lap when in 1844 he finally moved into Leventhorpe Hall, one of the great country houses of Yorkshire. It is a fine example of Georgian architecture, complete with extensive land, lodge and cottages. The hall still lies to the southeast of Leeds, on the north side of the River Aire, down river from Knostrop and close to the village of Swillington. In those days the grounds, amounting to 320 acres, swept down to the bank of the river and to Swillington Bridge, and the hall stood complete with both its two end wings. Leventhorpe Hall was built in 1774, designed by the renowned Yorkshire architect John Carr (1723-1807). For over fifty years, Carr was the most important architect in the north of England, with influence beyond. He had already built Harewood House in 1759, the home of Lord and Lady Harewood, Burlington House, Piccadilly, London in 1771 and several country houses for Yorkshire gentry. Leventhorpe Hall was built initially for Richard Green and later became the home of Thomas Ikin.

An impressive driveway approaches the hall, and as you pass through the front door, you enter the circular entrance hall, lit by a dome-shaped skylight, with an open 'flying' staircase leading to a galleried landing and eight main bedrooms. The thirty-six foot drawing room looks out onto a south-facing terrace from a large bay window, as do the dining room

Stair hall and flying staircase, Leventhorpe Hall, 1995. (Halifax Property Services)

and panelled library, each decorated with elaborate moulded plasterwork. Extensive cellars with vaulted ceilings make up the basement. The main building is much the same today as it was when it was built, but it has lost the two wings. In 1996, the building sold for around £600,000.

John Towlerton Leather was a practical, hard working civil engineer and not yet forty. He was away from Maria and their four children for considerable periods when he had to be on site at Chesterfield, Sheffield and Tadcaster. He was aware that Maria had been unhappy at Whittington, and even at Dam House she had drifted back to her family home at Knostrop. Leventhorpe was a healthy rural area, only five miles from Beeston Park and only three miles from Knostrop. JTL did not seem the sort of person to settle down as a member of the landed gentry, but this great opportunity came his way.

JTL's grandfather George Leather senior had been the chief engineer of the Fentons, so there were long associations and contacts between the two families. The Fentons

– so-called 'Coal Kings of Yorkshire' – included several generations of coal owners. Thomas Fenton the elder died in 1813 when son William took over the larger part of the coal mining inheritance, shared with his brother Thomas Fenton junior. Thomas Fenton died and by the 1830s the Fentons' great coal mining empire was drawing to a close. In 1837, William Fenton the Coal King himself who had resided at Thorpe Hall, Thorpe on the Hill, since about 1820, died and was buried in Wakefield Cathedral. With the passing of William Fenton, the whole family fortune, said to be worth £1,500,000, went to nephew Kirkby Fenton (Thomas' eldest son). On gaining the inheritance, Kirkby Fenton moved to Leventhorpe Hall and in the six years from 1837 to 1843, disposed of most of the Fenton's Yorkshire properties of coalmines, lands and farms. These included the large Wakefield Outwood, Methley, Crigglestone and Greaseborough collieries. The collieries that remained were Waterloo, situated less than a mile from Leventhorpe Hall, Whitkirk and Rothwell, in the same district, and Bagthorpe, Selston and one or two other pits in Nottinghamshire.

Late in 1843, Kirkby Fenton purchased the 530-acre estate of Charnwood Forest in Leicestershire, where he is said to have planted 100,000 trees to improve the beauty of the rugged landscape. He was more interested in fox hunting and sporting activities than the business side of life, and he left what remained of his Yorkshire holdings in the hands of John Towlerton Leather under the company name of 'Fenton and Leather'. JTL struck a good bargain, putting £3,500 into the Fenton and Leather venture and going on to organise the management of the collieries and remaining estates.

The Leather family moved in to their eight bedroom country mansion in the spring of 1844 an attractive bargain having been made. The four children, Ellen Eliza, Fred, Annie and Catherine Rosa were now aged nine, eight, five and three. The family required servants, a governess, a cook, groom, footman and gardener. The next four or five years was a period of a fairly stable and happy family life. Until disaster struck.

The Fenton and Leather partnership was a new period in the life of JTL. In the new business, the main income came from Waterloo colliery. This coalmine began life in 1815. Situated at Thorpe Stapleton on the Temple Newsam Estates close to the River Aire, it was purchased by William Fenton from Lady Irwin and was given its name because the first sod was dug on the eve of the Battle of Waterloo. Within the colliery several pits were opened, connected by a railway track that led to wharves on the canal – the Aire Calder Navigation. And there was a good market for the coals in Leeds. There was also the adjacent Thorpe Hall Iron Works with one blast furnace. Figures for 1847 give the annual output at 2,340 tons of pig iron, about 45 tons a week. In 1849, the works is listed simply as Leather and Co. The ore came from a bed of ironstone that occurs immediately above some of the coal seams, and two pits close to the river at Waterloo specialised in the working of ironstone.

Coalmining in the 1840s was a hard and dangerous life and something of the conditions and details of a mine accident may be of interest. By the standards of the time it seems J T Leather was an enlightened manager. Four years before JTL entered the Fenton-Leather partnership there was a disaster at Waterloo colliery, recorded in *The Leeds Intelligencer*. On the last day of January 1840 there occurred a big firedamp explosion in which three men were killed. They were Joseph Taylor age 26, Jonathan Robinson age 29, and Abraham Hargreaves 39. The accident was said to have been caused by the incorrect placing of a canvas sheet that guided the current of air in the right direction from one pit to another. Failure to do this allowed the methane gas to accumulate during the night. When the miners went in with their candles in the morning there was an immediate explosion. One of the men must have been running to safety and was found 90 yards from the explosion. The other two were following but had also been overcome. It was several hours before the bodies were reached. Two of the dead men left pregnant wives.

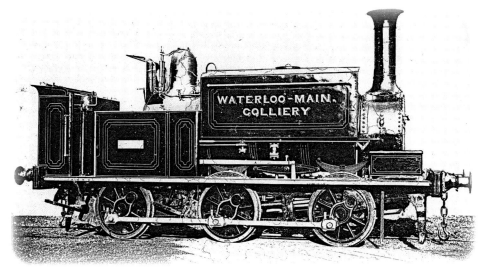

Steam locomotive Waterloo Main Colliery. This 0-6-0 saddle tank came from E B Wilson's Railway Foundry Hunslet in about 1854 to work at JTL's colliery. (L.H. Group Services Ltd)

Strikes by miners for higher wages occurred in most of the Yorkshire coalmines over the period from 1843 to 1845 and in December 1843 coalminers' strikes were beginning to affect the running of Waterloo colliery. An agreement was made between JTL, Mr Ingram of Temple Newsam and Leeds banker William Beckett to delay payments of colliery rents until things improved.

A report of the Children Employment Commissioners (Mines) in 1842 described conditions in coalmines in parts of Yorkshire, and revealed much brutality and squalor in the industry. The daily wage was 3 shillings and 6 pence for ten hours of labour, making a weekly wage of less than 24 shillings a week. The only two pits singled out for their more humanitarian ways were Middleton (the one that had the first steam railway) and Flockton (near Huddersfield). Flockton was, in fact, notable for child labour, including girls working underground. The main reason for using children was that the coal seams were only 2 feet 6 inches to 3 feet in thickness, the roof being too low for the use of pit ponies. Both children and miners had to crawl along passages only three feet high! The Coal Mines Regulation Act was passed as a direct result of this report and limited the employment of children to boys aged ten and over and prohibited all female labour underground. It is interesting to note that in the 1841 Census, there were at least a dozen people from families of the name Leather employed in the Flockton colliery, including a boy Jesse aged thirteen and fifteen-year-old Violet Leather. As the years went on there were many more Leather coalminers at Flockton. No relation can yet be found between these coalmining families and the engineering Leathers.

In a report of 1845, conditions at Fenton and Leather's Waterloo Colliery on the north bank of the River Aire were described as 'good with benevolent paternalism extended by the proprietors'. This referred to the fact that schools had been opened for miners' children, evening classes established for miners and, when the demand for coal was slack in the summer, the men were put to reclaiming the spoil land for agricultural use. These innovations were presumably due to the intervention of JTL.

In about 1850 JTL withdrew from the Kirkby Fenton partnership and opened up his own adjoining colliery at Waterloo Main on Pontefract Lane, so becoming the sole owner of a large colliery for the first time. The coalmining area on the Temple Newsam estate, which included both Waterloo and Waterloo Main collieries with scattered coal pits, also had coal seams that outcropped at the surface. Opencast coal was extracted by the laborious method of removing topsoil to uncover the seams. It was still being worked a hundred and thirty years later by means of powerful machinery.

In about 1848 or 49 a rail link was made from the Waterloo collieries to the Yorkshire and North Midland Railway at Neville Hill. Using the railway, JTL was able to send coal all over the north of England. This was in small quantities at first but, as Waterloo Main was extended, large quantities went to the station at Marsh Lane, Leeds. Offices were constructed on Pontefract Lane and railway lines from the pitheads of Waterloo and Waterloo Main led west to the wharves on the Knowsthorpe (or Knostrop) Cut as well as over the river at the wooden Waterloo Bridge to the Aire and Calder Navigation. JTL had had a close association with the Aire and Calder from his days as apprentice to George Leather. In 1858, JTL became a director of the Navigation, remaining one until his death. So he used all possible methods of transport. A branch line went almost directly to Knostrop New Hall, the home of George Leather, and served the village of Beeston. Knostrop was only a mile or so from JTL's home at Leventhorpe Hall along Pontefract Lane to the colliery offices, where he probably arrived on horseback. Thorpe iron works were working and the busy area became known as 't' back o' Leather's, a name which stayed well into the twentieth century. In 1999 the new link road

Knostrop New Hall, home of George Leather jnr and family. (photo Leeds Library and Information Service)

from the M1 to the A1 cut a swath through the old coalmining district, revealing coal seams and old workings.

Four more reservoirs for Sheffield By 1845, John Towlerton and his brother George Leather abandoned their contracting partnership with John Waring. This George Leather went into partnership with brother-in-law Charles Wetherell Wardle to found Victoria Pottery on part of the premises of Samuel Petty's Hunslet Hall Pottery. In the same year John Towlerton gave up his position as resident engineer and manager to the Sheffield Waterworks but he continued as the company's Consulting Engineer. The 1845 Sheffield Waterworks Act, passed in August, allowed four further dams to be constructed on the Pennine slopes west of Sheffield.

The gathering grounds are high on the moorland to the west of the city and range in elevation from 600 feet to 1,450 feet above sea level, with an annual rainfall of over forty inches. Because of the elevation, all the water entered the city by gravity so, although Sheffield is built on steep hillsides, there was no need for expensive pumping. The dams were the Upper and Lower Redmires embankments together with the Upper and Lower Rivelin. Three were started in 1846 but work on the larger Upper Redmires was postponed. The two dams on Rivelin Brook were both compensation reservoirs and were completed in 1848. These 'compensation dams' were to be used exclusively for the mill owners who had full control over them and power to draw from them as they wished to run their water-powered machinery. The dams compensated for the impounding of the waters of Wyming Brook. The Upper Rivelin dam is forty feet high, Lower Rivelin being sixty feet high and 335 yards long with about three times the capacity of the former (nearly 280 million cubic feet). Although John Towlerton Leather was the designer of the four dams, his resident engineer and manager was now John Gunson.

Lower Redmires was also begun in 1846. This was a storage reservoir forty feet high (capacity 210 million cubic feet). It was completed in 1849, but gave problems. During its construction, several slips of the embankment took place, which delayed things. In fact, in the winter of 1850-51 the reservoir had to be emptied for repairs. Geoffrey Binnie comments that it looked as if the fault was in the outlet culvert – water was getting through the culvert and washing away part of the embankment. According to Binnie, the spillway was a bold one for its time but he suspected the quality of cement and mortar in the stonework.

The much larger Upper Redmires was not completed until 1854. It was the highest so far at fifty-five feet with a storage capacity of 525 million cubic feet. When JTL designed it he omitted a tunnel and buried his pipelines in a trench in the foundations of the embankment. This may have been based on his experience with Lower Redmires. However, the water released through the pipelines was adequately controlled by sluices at the two inlets on the standpipe situated in the reservoir.

For details of the two final dams built by John Towlerton Leather, The Dale Dyke and Agden Dyke, both started in 1852, and the failure of the former in 1864, see chapter seven.

And two more big railway contracts In March 1846 JTL won the Erewash contract, a thirteen mile section of the North Midland Railway not far from Derby and Nottingham, where Swanwick was the engineer. JTL was fortunate to get the contract at all, but an error was found in the first accepted tender. He offered an amended tender at a much lower sum than his original and George Hudson, chairman of the Board, made a quick deal of the revised offer behind the Board's back. The contract was worth £107,290 and work was underway by June when JTL was advertising for a foreman to work in the Eastwood area, though by September the Board of Directors were expressing dissatisfaction at the progress being made. The section is mostly within Derbyshire but runs very close to the county boundary following the River Erewash from Long Eaton junction to Codnor Park Ironworks. It also serves the important industrial and coalmining district of the adjoining part of Nottinghamshire. Two steam locomotives used during the construction were the *Victoria*, made by Norris in 1839, and *Upton*, a Nasmyth Gaskell loco of 1841. A third one appears to have been a six-wheeled American locomotive[15]. These came

[15] Ian R Bendall, *Industrial Locomotives of Nottinghamshire* (Industrial Railway Society, 2000)

on from use on the Birmingham and Gloucester Railway. JTL is recorded as having purchased the *Upton* loco in March 1847. The first section of the line was opened on 6 September 1847 and the whole was completed in May 1849, when two locomotives were auctioned by JTL at Shipley Wharf.

In December 1847 the Board wanted one or two further works to be added to the Erewash line which JTL was reluctant to do unless the price was right. There were differences between the contractor and the engineer Swanwick as to the amounts for the extra work and in March 1849 Robert Stephenson was called in as mediator when £200 was advanced on account. But two years later there was still no settlement and JTL refused to accept the amount awarded by Robert Stephenson, so Mr Macauley was asked to enquire into the matter. Eventually in the summer of 1853 all was settled and payments made to the satisfaction of both parties.

On 21 January 1847 John Towlerton Leather won the Number One contract for the York and North Midland Railway, Leeds Extension Line. This, planned at the height of railway mania, was to run from Leeds to York, a distance of twenty-two miles The contract was for the 6½ mile stretch of line from Copmanthorpe, about four miles from the centre of York, to Tadcaster and was worth £54,500. Having satisfied the wishes of the landowners with support from Lord Harewood, the line received the required Act of Parliament on 26 June 1846. The route was competing with two other lines, the Leeds York & Midland Junction, and the Leeds and York,

Tadcaster Viaduct built 1846-1849 for the York and North Midland Leeds Extension, a beautiful monument to Contractor Leather.

and all of them wanted to cash in on the remunerative coal trade from the collieries at Garforth and Manston near Leeds. Of the three lines, one became superfluous and that was the Leeds Extension. When it was decided to abandon the contract, JTL claimed £14,250 in compensation. The Committee did not immediately accept this and in January 1850 the sum of £13,125 was offered, and accepted. The Leeds Extension was often referred to as Hudson's line as George Hudson – the 'Railway King' – was the chairman of the North Midland Railway.

By the time the decision was made to abandon the line JTL had built a fine eleven arch viaduct across the River Wharfe just above Tadcaster town plus a short three span bridge, which takes the road to Walton village over a cutting. The line was built north for about a mile to the supports of a proposed bridge over a stream known as The Foss. And that was as far as it got.

The viaduct over the Wharfe still stands in all its glory today, nearly 160 years later. It is built of a pale pinkish form of magnesian limestone and huge grey gritstone edgings with red brick lining beneath the arches, giving it a colourful aspect. Two magnificent central arches straddle the river and there are seven lofty round arches on the south side and two more on the north. The bridge is owned by Tadcaster town council and carries the 'Viaduct walk' but the parapets are so high there is no view from it. In 1882 a line was laid over the viaduct to serve a corn mill for a few years on the north bank of the river, though since 1955 the bridge has not been used to carry goods, though it does carry large water mains. The viaduct is one of only a few of JTL's projects that still stand today. There is something about a viaduct that must have had great appeal to the contractor. It required far more talent and ingenuity to build than an embankment or cutting and needed the help of highly skilled masons and builders. It is an awe-inspiring monument.

Detail of stonework in the Tadcaster Viaduct.

Other railway contracts tendered by John Towlerton Leather were Knottingley Bridge on the Yorkshire North Midland Railway, costed at £49,867, which went to William Hutchinson at £43,500, and in January 1852, Barnsley Bridge on the Manchester, Sheffield and Lincolnshire Railway, tendered at £38,000 but taken by George Miller at £34,566. A decade later in March 1863 JTL put in for the Runcorn Bridge on the London and North Western Railway for the hefty sum of £382,941 – his final railway tender. The contract went initially to William McCormick for £357,552, then to the well-known contractor Thomas Brassey who carried out the work, completed in 1868. This important bridge across the River Mersey consists of three 300-foot spans of wrought iron double-web lattice girders on stone piers, carrying the railway 75 feet above the river.

It is interesting to note that back in 1847 JTL put in a tender for the building of the wet dock at Jarrow[16], involving George Hudson and the railways of the region, when an Act of Parliament for a 40 acre dock was obtained. The tender of £139,670 was accepted when others ranged to £191,000. JTL soon discovered that there were errors in his tender and withdrew, the work being awarded then to contractor Richard Cail for £148,000.

Early in 1846, Maria gave birth to their second son Arthur Hugo Leather, her sixth and last baby. He was born at Leventhorpe Hall on 30th March. Arthur Hugo later shunned his father's efforts to set him up in business, married money, changed his surname and lived to be 78.

Barely three years after the birth of her sixth child when Maria was only 37 she became ill and finally contracted pneumonia. She struggled for three weeks and sadly died on 22 January 1849. JTL and Maria had been married for seventeen years. They had known each other closely all their lives and most of the time got on very well together. But though happy to start with, the marriage had been a struggle for them both. JTL had been away a lot and, at Sheffield and Whittington, Maria had been isolated from the rest of her family and had paid frequent visits to her father's home at Knostrop. Two weeks after Maria's death, their eight-year-old daughter Catherine Rosa died of scarlet fever.

[16] R W Rennison, Newcomen Society Transactions, v.70, n.2, 1998-99, pp 161-183.

Portland Breakwater

The spring of 1849 saw a major change in the life of John Towlerton Leather. The shock of the deaths of his wife Maria, at only thirty-seven and Catherine Rosa, their eight year old daughter, coming so suddenly one after the other, was overwhelming, perplexing and exhausting. In the autumn, his father James Leather died at the age of 70, at the family home at Parkside Beeston. The death of Mary his mother came nine months later. Mary had also reached three score years and ten and both were buried in Beeston churchyard, where the solid square block of stone bearing their names still exists. In his will, James left 'under £2,000'. The house and other properties at Beeston went to sons George and William Henry. Since JTL and his sister Liz – now married to Charles Wardle – were well off enough not to need further support, they were not provided for in the will. In fact Liz and her engineer husband and children now lived at 'The Park' adjacent to 'Parkside'.

But it was early in 1849 when the big change came for JTL. The contract for the Leeds Extension railway suddenly ended and the future outlook had shifted completely. He might get away from Leeds and take on something quite different. He could leave his four children, two at Leventhorpe Hall in the care of his trusted servants, and two away at school – and his cousins at Knostrop were not far away. The total commitment of being involved in a new project would take his mind off his tragic loss – and the opportunity was there. He tendered for a huge contract: that of the construction of the Portland breakwater in Dorset under the direction of the Admiralty, and in the early summer of 1849 he was appointed sole contractor – 'Contractor of Public Works' – where James Meadows Rendel was chief engineer. The vast undertaking of building 1.6 miles of breakwaters at a cost of over £1 million was to engage J T Leather for a period of seventeen years from 1849 to 1866. It was to be the peak of his career, his proudest work.

The bay at Portland was already sheltered by Chesil Beach to the west and the Isle of Portland to the south, thus protected from prevailing south-westerly winds. It was a fine natural anchorage which only needed cover from strong winds in the south-east to make it an excellent 'harbour of refuge'. There was little existing shelter for ships along 120 miles of the English Channel coast between Plymouth and Portsmouth

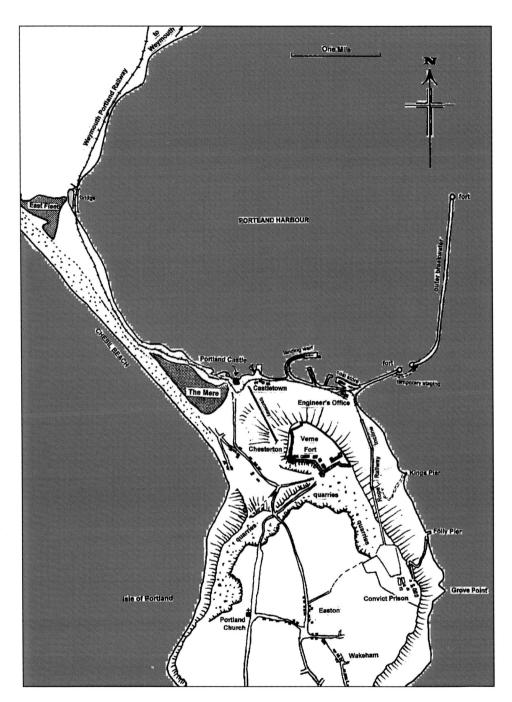

Map showing the position of the Portland Breakwater in relation to the Isle of Portland and the source of quarried stone and the Convict Prison.

and this was another point in its favour. The seabed had an even depth of about 50 feet at lowest tides and was made up of hard Kimmeridge clay (of Jurassic age), excellent for securing an anchor.

In 1843 a Royal Commission had been appointed to consider the matter, a detailed survey was made of the seabed, and a report in May 1844[17] heartily recommended a breakwater at Portland. The scheme had the support of the Prime Minister and Sir Robert Peel. The Royal family were also more than interested in the project. In 1846, Prince Albert, the Prince Consort, and Queen Victoria were aboard the royal yacht when they had to take shelter in the bay during a storm and Prince Albert followed the plans for the building of a breakwater with close interest. (During its construction His Royal Highness was to visit the site on six occasions.) The Act of Parliament for the Portland Breakwater came in May 1847. The harbour of refuge that the breakwater would enclose was to be the largest area of deep water of any artificial harbour in Great Britain – over three square miles – and of great national importance. The very successful civil engineer, James Meadows Rendel, was to be assisted by resident engineer John Coode.

Prisoners at work in the quarries at Portland where hundreds were employed in this traditional convict occupation, helping to reduce overall costs of the breakwater. The island situation was ideal for a prison. (Weymouth Library)

The construction of a breakwater at Portland had further advantages. A decision by the government, at the same time as the breakwater Act, to make the island of Portland a penal settlement and to employ convicts on the breakwater was a shrewd one. There was a desperate need for more prison accommodation as transportation of criminals was being resisted in the colonies and the employment of hundreds of convicts on the breakwater would reduce costs of labour. The island was an ideal site for a prison, and prisoners would mainly be working the quarries – traditional convict work. The prison was also an experiment in employing prisoners on public

[17] Report of the Commissioners of Refuge and Harbours, 1844.

works to give them work experience prior either to release or to transportation. A natural advantage for the building of the breakwater was the large amount of Portland stone readily available, much of it easily removed rubble discarded by former quarry working. The island also had natural springs, which could provide water not only for use during the building of the breakwater but later on to supply ships using the harbour. Lastly, Portland Island was regarded as a natural defensive site ideal for a naval base, and rumblings and rumours about militant French and the men of war in Cherbourg harbour only intensified the decision in favour.

Civil Engineer James Meadows Rendel was a West Country man, born in Oakhampton Devon, who had studied under Thomas Telford. He was very experienced in bridge design, and was the first to use hydraulic machinery in a swing bridge. As early as 1822 he designed the Saltash suspension bridge across the Tamar in Devon. He introduced a system of steam-driven chain ferry, and was employed in designing docks and harbours up and down the country. For the five-arch cast iron Lara Bridge at Plymouth, opened in 1827, he received the Telford Medal. It was while he was inspecting the construction of Lara Bridge, that he fell from the scaffolding into the sea. Wearing a heavy coat and jackboots he was submerged for some time before being rescued. It is said that while under the water Rendel's life flashed before him in the minutest detail.

The three-stage incline (two are visible) from the quarries to the start of the Breakwater. (detail from engraving made from Carmichael's oil painting)

James Rendel's resident engineer was to be John Coode, civil engineer from Cornwall who had been apprenticed to Rendel in Plymouth. The Portland breakwater was his first major work, which he took over as chief engineer on Rendel's death in 1856. He soon became an authority on harbour construction, and was knighted on the completion of the Portland breakwater. Colonial governments all over the world consulted him. After Portland, the other achievement he was best known for was the great harbour of Colombo in Ceylon (Sri Lanka) – built between 1874 and 1875.

At Portland, Rendel first planned a railway incline from the quarries down to the beginning of the breakwater. Work began in August 1847 when Rigby and Co. were the contractors for the incline. By November they were employing 550 men on the rope railway which led for almost a mile from the quarries on Portland heights, over 300 feet above the sea, down the steep cliff-side to the breakwater with an extension along the Castletown waterfront. The two parallel railway tracks descended in three stages with galvanised steel ropes winding round revolving drums at the top of each; the slope was one in ten for the upper and lower sections with the more gentle gradient of one in fifteen on the central section. The weight of the loaded wagons that came down the incline drew up the empty ones on the parallel line. At the top was a weighbridge (designed by Napiers of Lambeth) which recorded the tonnage of stone as each wagon passed over it, each wagon carrying from six to ten tons of rough stone. The convicts started to arrive in 1848 and worked initially on the prison accommodation, barracks and the incline. After that they worked mainly in the stone quarries, there being between 600 and 900 men employed there during much of the building of the breakwater.

A start on the breakwater itself was made in 1849 and by July was advanced enough to render the laying of a foundation stone. This took place on Wednesday 25 July, by his Royal Highness Prince Albert, Prince Consort. After visiting Dorchester and Weymouth, the Prince crossed the bay on his yacht, the *Victoria and Albert*. Captain C A Manning and others received him at noon together with a salute of twenty-one guns. The Prince addressed the people of Portland in the following words:

> 'The work, of which I am about to lay the foundation stone, whilst it is of great national importance as forming a secure Harbour of Refuge for ships of the Royal Navy, and for Merchant Vessels freighted with commerce of the whole world, will, I trust, be also of especial service to this neighbourhood, by increasing its trade, and spreading employment among its labouring population.'

Following the speeches, James Rendel read the inscription on the brass plate fixed to the foundation stone, which gave the date and named the engineers. A sealed bottle containing the plans and a set of coins of the realm were cemented inside the prepared stone and riveted by John Coode. Prince Albert moved a lever that released the huge stone,

> 'and it fell with immense force into the sea and thus lodged in its destined resting place. A Royal salute was fired and the bands struck up *Rule Britannia*. A waggon was brought loaded with stone, which was shot immediately over the sunken stone. Many hearty and deafening cheers were given for the Prince, who was then conducted by Admiral Sir Bladen Capel, Mr Rendel, Captain Manning and others to the carriage which had been constructed to convey His Royal Highness by a tram-road to the Portland Prison. The train, covered in crimson material, was drawn up a very steep ascent by means of ropes on drums and preceded at a slow pace. The scene presented from the summit of this railroad, as the eye looked back on the thousands of persons following the train, the tastefully ornamented spot where the Prince had lately stood, the flags and banners fluttering in the breeze, the gaily dressed vessels, and the splendid bay and noble range of hills... can never be forgotten by the thousands who witnessed it.
>
> All the workmen employed on the public works, to the number of 300, sat down to a substantial dinner at Portland about 4-o'clock, under a well-constructed and spacious tent.'[18]

It is not stated in this report whether John Towlerton Leather was present, but it was most likely. He had just been appointed contractor and may have begun work on the project. The initial stages that had been started two years earlier predominantly involved the incline, which Prince Albert had ridden on.

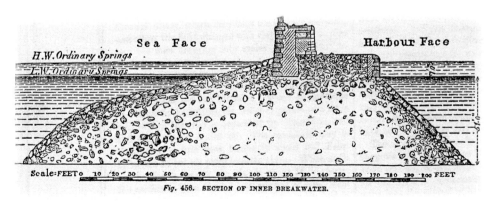

Section across the first part of the Breakwater showing construction details. (drawing by the Breakwater Engineer John Coode in Cyclopaedia of Useful Arts 1860s)

[18] *Dorset County Chronicle* 26 July 1859

J T Leather engaged Edward Pease Smith as his Resident Manager. This was the man who had worked with him on the Chesterfield contract of the North Midland Railway and who was a close friend and associate over many years. Edward Pease Smith, born in Croydon of a Quaker family, was also a civil engineer and took a major part in the proceedings, introducing many original designs and features in the breakwater works. He designed a water supply system for the works, bringing water up from the south side of the island by means of an efficient steam pump, which he devised himself. He also isolated the Verne fortifications by a dramatic and deep cutting in the solid rock, 100 feet wide and 75 feet deep. This was begun in 1850 and the large amount of stone from this excavation was used for the breakwater. E P Smith also carried out work in steepening the Verne rock to make it more impregnable. During this time he directed the construction of works for the Weymouth Waterworks that included drainage within the town. Between the four of them, Rendel, Coode, Leather and Smith, there was so much in the way of inventive and resourceful ideas, civil engineering experience, and total dedication as to make the whole massive project not only possible but also immensely successful.

The breakwater itself was a considerable feat of practical engineering, requiring all the latest technology and expertise available. An enormous temporary wooden staging was erected, 120 feet wide, which followed the line of the breakwater out into the bay. It was built on huge ninety-foot piles driven into the seabed. The staging carried five parallel railway tracks of the broad, seven-foot gauge, in general use by Brunel in southwest England. It was planning on a big scale. Special hopper wagons with bottom openings and shoots were made enabling stone to be tipped directly into the sea. Each wagon, carrying up to ten tons of stone, had a tilting floor. When the iron pin was knocked out, the weight of the stone tilted the floor and dropped between the rails and into the sea. Once emptied, the weighted rear of the floor swung it back into position. As each bay of the pier was completed, the great timber piles became concealed by the thick heap of rock rubble – and the timbers are still there today, buried deep in the breakwater.

By June 1850 the staging had reached 150 yards from the shore. Stuart Morris[19] describes how 'men were working suspended on a small seat "only a few feet above the water which foams beneath them", each great pile took ten men three hours to screw into the sea bed'. 'J T Leather spared no expense on mechanical innovation. He had a gigantic crane constructed on a movable platform and a 100ft long pressure chamber was made in which creosote was forced to the heart of the great timbers used for the temporary staging.' The piles, weighing seven or eight tons, were made of wood, square in section and measuring 14 by 22 inches. They were bolted and

---

[19] *Portland, an Illustrated History*, Stuart Morris (Dovecote Press, 1985).

The Great Breakwater at Portland. The engraving from the Illustrated London News shows how the temporary staging, carrying up to five parallel railway tracks, bypasses the forts to serve the longer and second leg of the breakwater. In the foreground are the coal wharves, the Engineer's Office and food store.

bound together with iron bands. At the tip was a cast iron socket connected by a five-inch diameter wrought iron bar to a two foot six, cast iron 'Mitchell' screw, enabling it to be turned and fixed into the hard clay seabed. At the upper end a cap was attached with long radiating wooden arms. The arms were notched to take a rope fixed to a capstan. As the pile was lowered and turned into place, the rope uncoiled from the arms on the pile until the screw bit firmly some six or eight feet into the clay. Rows of piles were thus fitted every thirty feet.[20] Every third set of

Detail from Carmichael's oil painting showing the staging complete with steam train, cranes and hoists, and indicating the impressive scale and industry of the operations.

[20] *Cyclopaedia of Useful Arts*, Vol. III, ed. Charles Tomlinson (London, Virtue, 1860s).

piles were double timbers measuring 22 by 26 inches. Cross tie rods and horizontal beams connected one pile to the adjacent one.

A third of a million tons of limestone was quarried for the Breakwater just in 1851 – over 1,000 tons of stone daily. At the peak it was stated that 2,000 to 3,000 tons of stone per day were transported along the staging and added to the breakwater. Trainloads, first pulled by horses, then by steam engines, were going back and forth all day long and, in the summer months, work continued into the night to speed up progress. Large blocks, each weighing up to six tons, were dropped and smaller material filled the gaps between. The flowing of the tide helped to settle the stone ready for the next layer.

By the middle of 1851 the staging was 300 yards out into the bay and into deeper water, where, fifty feet under the sea, divers, in suits made of leather, rubber and copper, guided the huge piles as they were driven into the seabed. They also placed large stones at the foot of the piles to hold them more securely. Visitors came from all over Europe. They could walk along a walkway on the staging and view the divers working under water. 'The divers remain down at their cold, dark work, sometimes in a depth of 70 feet, for a whole tide, even when the sea is rough and tumbling heavily, and they can see by the fluctuations in the gloomy twilight how the waves are rolling above their heads. Only one accident has occurred among these men during the progress of the works, but that was, of course, fatal.'

Although his services were required on site at Portland, where apart from his office he now had a house built for his personal use, J T Leather had important commitments at his colliery in Leeds. He made frequent trips back and forth between Portland and Leeds and, in the ten-year census at the end of March 1851, he is recorded at home in Leventhorpe Hall described as civil engineer and contractor, age 46. With him is his five-year old son Arthur Hugo who is being educated at home by a governess. Servants at the hall include a footman, cook, nurse, and housemaid. The Leeds directory for the same year has J T Leather as 'coal owner of Leventhorpe Hall', and two years later as 'colliery owner, Waterloo Main Colliery, Pontefract Lane, Leeds.'

While in Leeds J T Leather made enquires at E B Wilson's Railway Foundry in Hunslet for the possibility of using steam engines not only at his colliery but on the breakwater at Portland. His engineer son-in-law Charles Wardle was already employed there as chief cashier and in charge of the stationary engine shop. J T Leather ordered a 0-4-0 tank engine with four foot driving wheels named *Queen*. It was the first locomotive to be used on the breakwater and was delivered in 1852. A second tank engine from the Railway Foundry for the breakwater was purchased in 1854. In the same year two further locomotives came into service on the breakwater, making five in total up to that time. The works brought further steam engines into use as building proceeded, and it is possible one or two came on from J T Leather's colliery at Waterloo Main, near Leeds.

By the spring of 1852, three years had gone by since his wife Maria had died and, as a man in his position with a young family, he needed a wife to look after them and manage his large home. He had known the Spencer Page family some ten years earlier when he was in Whittington, working on the Chesterfield contract, and had met their daughter Harriet. She was now thirty-three and he forty-seven. He decided to visit their estate at Shirland in Derbyshire.

Harriet Spencer Page was beautiful and co-heiress to her father's estate. There was no need for a prolonged engagement and, on 19 May 1852, the marriage took place of John Towlerton Leather and Harriet Spencer Page in the parish church of Morton, near Alfreton, Derbyshire. JTL established his new wife at Leventhorpe Hall, and no doubt spent more time in Yorkshire than he had until then. On 27 September 1853 Spencer Towlerton Leather was born, but sadly sixteen months later on 3 February 1855 the young boy died – Harriet's only son. Then, a year later came the birth of their second child, Edith, who lived well into the next century.

By July of 1852, J T Leather was back in Portland where there was an unexpected royal visit to the breakwater by Prince Albert and Prince Alfred aboard the royal

Oil paintings of Harriet Leather (née Spencer Page) and John Towlerton Leather c1854

- 54 -

yacht. The party was received by John Coode and conducted to the end of the breakwater staging where the engineering operations were explained. The staging was then approaching half a mile from the shore and the part filled up with stone was already providing considerable shelter for anchored vessels. A news item the following January refers to 140 ships sheltering in the 'Portland Roads' – from stormy conditions out at sea. The Illustrated London News for 17th July tells how well the work is progressing, with the steam boat *Princess* being used on contract work.

'Construction of the Portland Breakwater,' an oil painting by J W Carmichael measuring 66 by 40 inches, commissioned by J T Leather in 1853. (photo Royal Exchange Art Gallery, London)

By March 1853 Contractor Leather required further amounts of quality stone and opened his own quarry at Cheyne, on the north end of the island of Portland, where roachstone, a type not available in the convict quarries, was extracted. The stone has a high shell content and a rough finish. It was ideal for the large-scale work on the breakwater where massive blocks were required. He also brought granite from Cornwall to make a smooth facing layer against the sea. From the quarry at Cheyne he built a rail incline to take the stone to the breakwater and marked the completion of the 100th bay of piles in May 1853 by acquiring a very fine new steam paddle yacht for his personal use. He was also looking out for a steam tug for contracting work.

Work progresses on the staging with a huge timber pile being manoeuvred into place and JTL's steam yacht Princess standing by. (ILN)

1853 was a good year for J T Leather and he was feeling on top of the world when he commissioned Tyneside artist John Wilson Carmichael to produce a large oil painting of the breakwater. It would show the works in progress, the massive staging, the stone-carrying trains steaming back and forth; there would also be the

JTL's paddle steamer Princess working on the Breakwater construction. (detail from the engraving of Carmichael's oil painting)

great sailing ships, the steamers used on the works and, in the background the cliffs of the Isle of Portland with the quarries and the incline. The finished painting was magnificent. What a proud moment it was for JTL. It was vital that he should record the progression of the works, as in the end, the staging and all the action would be gone forever. The picture measured five and a half feet by three feet four inches. He was so pleased with it that he had an engraving made from it, so that friends and family could have a copy to hang on their walls. Family tradition has it that it was his paddle steamer in the centre of the picture and he is said to be the one on the bridge wearing the top hat![21]

'The Defences of Portland Harbour', the first fort with Verne Fortress in the background. A walkway was included between the railway tracks for visitors to view the construction of the Breakwater. The rail tracks here curve around the fort between the two sections of the breakwater. (Illustrated Times, 9 August 1862)

In October of 1853 J T Leather purchased, from the Cosens brothers, the steamer *Princess* which he used to control the Breakwater operations. This paddle steamer was built in 1844 in London and came to Weymouth in 1849. It was used regularly by Captain Joseph and Captain William Cosens both as a ferryboat on contract work and for special excursions. JTL kept it until April 1857 when it went to Plymouth to run excursions on the River Tamar. The *Princess* appears in the *Illustrated London*

---

[21] In 2004 the newly cleaned painting was exhibited at the Royal Exchange Art Gallery in London with a price tag of £140,000.

News illustration. The Cosens brothers did very good business carrying workmen and the thousands of tourists who came to view the works. They also provided steamers to tow stone barges and undertake breakwater work for JTL. After the *Princess*, the steamers *Prince, Contractor, Ocean Pride* and others were added to the Cosens' working fleet. J T Leather later acquired another steamer called *Contractor*, which was used at Portland. She was built in 1857 at Shields and came to Weymouth on 25th March 1861 under JTL's ownership. He kept her until January 1866 when she was wrecked while engaged in the building of the Spithead forts and a severe storm struck the Solent[22]. Probably from this steamer came two small brass signal canons. For many years they stood in front of the house at Middleton – and a ship's wheel decorated the office there. Early In 1859 JTL purchased another steam yacht named *Ceres*[23].

On Coronation Day July 1854, when the first stone of the facing of the inner pier had appeared above water, Contractor Leather gave a substantial dinner to eighty of his divers and other workmen. The *Dorset County Chronicle* added that their reporter had met up with an eminent Russian engineer who had been on a short visit to Portland who spoke in the highest terms of the 'magnificent breakwater'. Several well-known visitors came to see the works over the years, and such a one was the Italian leader General Garibaldi, in 1864. Visitors were positively encouraged to see the progress of the breakwater and a drawing from the *Illustrated Times* for 9 August 1862 shows tourists in top hats and crinoline gowns walking unconcernedly between the railway lines. Some visitors noticed that, lying among the stones, were occasional giant fossil ammonites up to two feet across. The Breakwater had become Dorset's major tourist attraction.

A light breeze welcomed Prince Albert on his next visit in September 1854. John Coode took him in a crimson-covered truck on 'a minute inspection of the stupendous structure comparing at almost every step its progress with plans in the hands of the engineer'. The Dorset County Chronicle continues as follows:

> 'No sooner had the *Victoria and Albert* appeared off Portland than the news spread, by the aid of the bellman, that the Queen had arrived and landed at the Breakwater! Yachts were quickly under sail, together with boats of every description, making all possible speed for Portland. Shortly after twelve-o'clock the *Contractor* steamer left with a large company, followed directly by the *Prince* steamer conveying another numerous party. These steamers rounded the *Victoria and Albert* at the very moment Prince Albert was departing from the Breakwater. On leaving the works, his Royal Highness accompanied as before, undertook the laborious task of walking the steep

---

[22] Information from personal correspondence with Richard Clammer of Chepstow.
[23] Letter from Harriet to JTL, 11 May 1859

range of hills, in the direction of the new barracks and government quarries. The Prince and party returned to the Breakwater by way of the inclined plane, about three-o'clock, and as the royal boat left, cheers rounded on all sides, ashore and afloat.'

Being a contractor on such a large scale was a risky business. J T Leather's company had most of its assets sunk in the temporary staging, as well as in the steam engines, steam boats and steam cranes, all of which could succumb to natural disaster or accidents of human error. Over the years the company had some losses, though considering the time scale, the loss of human life was small. However, an accident in November 1853 resulted in the death of two workmen. 'An engine was pushing forwards four loaded stone waggons and when it reached the opening, a pile sank and, one after another the waggons and the engine fell into the water. Eight men were immersed, two of whom were crushed and drowned and the stoker had three of his fingers smashed; all the rest were more or less bruised. The two men who perished (named Gard and Woolley) were unmarried.' The following week's news reported that the four wagons and engine had been 'taken up' but the bodies, it was supposed, were covered by the stone from the wagons.

Portland was benefiting in several ways by the presence of the big engineers. In 1856 J T Leather, John Coode and Captain Manning founded a Mechanics Institute in Portland where workers could improve their learning and hear lectures by visiting and local speakers of the latest scientific achievements. John Coode had become fascinated by the natural feature of Chesil Beach, which links the island of Portland to the coast, a phenomenon known as a tombolo. He wrote a definitive paper on its formation for the Institution of Civil Engineers, describing this large 15 mile long coastal landform, and explaining the reason for the sorting of the pebbles, very small at the western, Abbotsbury end and much larger at the Portland end.

There were further accidents and storm damage that continued to encumber the engineers. In October 1855, a wooden lighthouse at the end of the staging was burnt down, but was replaced by a bright red 'jack in the basket' lantern. As the breakwater was growing out to sea, it became a hazard in itself and several vessels foundered on it. In April 1858 a storm wrecked five complete pile bays – 150 feet of staging – tossing the huge timbers like matchsticks and abandoning them miles along the shore. In 1859 gigantic seas ripped open a 200-foot gap in the staging, which must have taken several weeks to replace. In May of the same year 'a poor fellow named Waters lost his life. It appears that the unfortunate man was riding on a trolley (a wagon constructed without sides and used for the purpose of conveying worked stone on to the Breakwater) when by some means the wagon ran off the rails and was precipitated onto the stone below, the deceased falling underneath. A verdict of Accidental Death was returned.' Two years later, on a line skirting the Verne fortifications an engine, pulling several wagons, rounded a sharp curve and met a line of loaded stone wagons coming rapidly the other way on the same line down the incline. The engine driver and stoker jumped clear as the two trains smashed into each other. The engine was totally shattered. In 1862 a steam crane and wagons were thrown into the sea. In trying to recover them, the tackle broke and all the equipment fell again to the bottom. The Illustrated London News (12 October 1861) adds a sympathetic note:

> 'In operations of this kind where a great battle has to be fought with the sea, which will sometimes, in a dark winter night, enraged and furious, rush headlong in upon incomplete works and the temporary appliances used to construct them, catching those in charge unawares and sweeping away many thousands of pounds' worth of property in a single hour, we ought not to forget the contractor, on whom those losses fall, with all the anxiety, disappointment, and trouble which such calamities bring about. The engineers have their difficulties to overcome, and the contractor is not without his troubles, as Mr J T Leather, of Leeds, would no doubt tell us, he having executed the whole of these important works.'

On the positive side there were far more occasions when things went well. There were exciting times when it was touch and go whether the buoyant staging would hold, or whether the last lot of stone would stay against the strong spring tides. The whole construction of this sea wall was a brilliant example of man controlling nature. This was one of the tenets of the civil engineer. Man was the master and nature could be tamed and disciplined.

The Prince of Wales landing at Weymouth. (ILN)

As the breakwater progressed Prince Albert paid another informal visit, accompanied by Prince Alfred and Prince Arthur. On 25 July 1859 the royal yacht anchored and the party transferred to the royal barge, which was greeted by John Coode and Contractor Leather and crowds of cheering men.

> 'In spite of the heat the Verne Heights were speedily scaled. The busy scene presented here, more especially the stupendous excavations for the dry ditch of the fort was striking in the extreme. Hundreds of men were at work,

locomotive engines, horses, iron waggons, cranes and winches, all in motion. Everything constructed on a colossal scale and amidst the seeming confusion of the varied operations going on, the utmost order and regularity can be detected. Nearly 1,000 tons of hard rock are obtained from this excavation and deposited daily on the Breakwater, along with an even greater quantity from the convict quarries.'

Prince Albert went on to inspect the breakwater with John Coode and Prince Alfred and Prince Arthur rode out in the royal carriage to the end of the breakwater, just over a mile and a quarter in extent, under the guidance of E P Smith and Mr Beaufort, assistant engineer to the Admiralty.

James Meadows Rendel FRS became President of the Institution of Civil Engineers for 1852 and 1853. He was designing new projects right up to his early death in November 1856 at the age of 57. His later work included the suspension bridge at Inverness and the swing bridge at Wisbech, both of which J T Leather was involved with as contractor. On the death of James Rendel, John Coode was immediately asked to take over the full responsibility of the Portland works as chief engineer.

In 1859 came the sudden and tragic death of J T Leather's adored wife Harriet. She was involved in an accident with her horse and waggonette. It was one day short of their eighth wedding anniversary and she was still only 39. On Thursday afternoon 18 May 1859 Harriet, accompanied by her three year old daughter Edith, Annie, now 20, and the two Wardle nieces, Addie and Minnie from Leeds, were on an outing to Wakefield. When the party reached Stanley, near Wakefield, about four miles from Leventhorpe Hall, the horse Harriet was driving took fright at something and suddenly bolted. The waggonette was flung violently against the corner of a house and completely overturned, throwing everybody to the ground. Although none of the others was seriously hurt, Harriet hit her head badly and suffered concussion. She was taken to a nearby house where she lay in a coma until she died the next day. Ten years earlier JTL's first wife Maria had died at the age of 37. This was history repeating itself. JTL had now lost two wives in their prime and four of the eight children born to him.

At Christmas that year JTL sent a moving letter to three-year-old Edith who had survived the accident. She was his only link to Harriet and she was always special for him:

My little darling Edith,

The earnest prayer of thy poor bereaved father, my sweet little darling, is that you may grow up by the grace of our Lord in all goodness in the likeness and after the example of thy sainted mother—who altho' lost to us in this life, let us hope that we may meet her hereafter in that world where neither sin nor sorrow can be known. We may one and all wish you my darling a "merry Christmas" for happily it is far beyond thy young mind to comprehend the bitterness of the affliction which the loss of thy dear mother inflicts upon her unhappy husband.

That every blessing of this life may be extended to you my sweet darling and that you may be received into the Kingdom of Heaven hereafter is the sincere and hopeful prayer of your Father,

J Towlerton Leather

The J T Leather Coat of Arms has 'water' added in the position of the middle star to represent the hydraulic engineer. He also had a separate coat of arms for his wife Harriet.

Ironically about a week before Harriet was killed in the horse and waggonette accident, John Towlerton Leather and his wife were each granted their coat of arms. J T Leather had applied to the Duke of Norfolk, who had the position of Hereditary Marshal of England. The 'arms and crest' show a 'demi lion rampant', being the top half of a lion standing upright. It has three six-pointed stars on its shoulder and holds between its paws a 'fountain' – a circle with waves on it, indicating water. This last bit is specifically for the hydraulic engineer. The shield below has a diagonal band in silver on gold with another 'fountain' between two six-pointed stars. The Latin motto *'nil nisi quod honestum'*, meaning 'nothing but that which is honest' adorns the crest. The coat of arms destined for Harriet's children was similar but included the Spencer Page shield in the centre, which bore two roses and a bird. The arms were to be borne by J T Leather and his wife and their descendants. The crest is a modification of an existing coat of arms first used as far as we know in the large stained glass window of St Peter's parish church, Leeds. It is dated 1856 with the name of George Leather below it.

After the accident with horse and trap, JTL's daughter Annie made herself responsible for bringing up the child Edith who, 28 years later, was to marry Colonel Charles Falkiner Morton. Annie was very much part of JTL's household and years later, JTL's letters to his grandson often mentioned Aunt Annie. She must have been a great support for him. She never married and died at her home in Beaufort Gardens, Kensington in 1910, at the age of 71.

In the summer of 1860 Contractor Leather decided he would take a break, and taking with him his 21 year old daughter Annie, had a most successful and memorable trip to Wiesbaden on the Rhine. Years later he recollects seeing cousins at Wiesbaden, listening to charming music, and in a beautiful forest half way between Wiesbaden and Schalbach seeing some deer and gathering wild strawberries. On another occasion, in 1870, JTL made a trip to Rome where he ordered a marble table to be made by the sculptor Leonardi for his Northumberland home.

In the early 1860s, while busier than ever on the south coast, it was apparent to JTL that a base in London would be extremely useful, a place where he could stay, take his breath, meet people, even lobby MPs, attend functions and generally feel at the centre of

This is number 18 Carlton House Terrace today. Number 19, J T Leather's London address, is no longer in existence but no doubt had a similar imposing facade. In the 1860s The Duke and Duchess of Newcastle lived here at number 18. (photo B D Leather)

things. He was soon in possession of number 19 Carleton House Terrace, a most prestigious address, in the best part of town – next to Pall Mall and St James Park. Here he found among his neighbours many titled statesmen and members of the aristocracy. The post office directory of 1869 shows a formidable list of people including prime minister William Ewart Gladstone at number 11, and the Duke and Duchess of Newcastle at number 18. The list also includes Lord Frederick Charles Cavendish who had entered Parliament as a Liberal MP for the West Riding of Yorkshire.

Sir Matthew White Ridley, fourth Baronet of Blagdon, Northumberland, was at number 10. Sir Matthew was an enthusiastic patron of the Northumbrian sculptor John Graham Lough (1798-1876). John Towlerton Leather had purchased

'John Towlerton Leather's Achievements', marble plaque by Northumbrian sculptor John Graham Lough with detail the head of JTL (inset).
J G Lough's 'low relief' sculpture depicts John Towlerton Leather sitting on a rock surmounting the waves – an allusion to his engineering achievements at Portland, Spithead and Portsmouth. He holds a scroll in one hand and appears to be calming the waves with the other. He is surrounded by four maidens, naked cherubs, four horses with serpents' tails, and Neptune below the sea, reclining on a shell. On the left is the inverted figure of a woman whose feet become forked tails, while a female figure on the right tumbles in the waves. Just what did JTL make of it all? There he was, the successful engineer of the nineteenth century, portrayed at the centre of a rich classical Lough design. In fact when the plaque arrived at Middleton Hall he never opened the packaging.

sculptures from Lough but, somewhat mysteriously, the sculptor also presented him with a large circular marble plaque featuring JTL himself. It is probable that the unusual plaque was a gift from Sir Matthew, who was both a patron of the sculptor and a great admirer of the engineer. The three men of Northumberland, Ridley, Lough and Leather are thus bound up in a fascinating way. The plaque now resides in the Laing Art Galley in Newcastle upon Tyne.

It was in 1864 that JTL was fully taken up with the aftermath of the failure of his highest dam at Sheffield, the Dale Dyke Dam for which see Chapter 6.

In Portland, by 1866 the last phase of the breakwater was in progress. It concerned the building of two armed forts and it was planned to erect one at each end of the two lengths of breakwater. At the outer end of the first breakwater is the smaller 'Inner Pier Fort', which faces the gap known as South Ship Channel. Construction began in 1859 and was completed three years later. The fort is separated from the breakwater by a narrow gap and reached by a wooden drawbridge. It is 100 feet in diameter and finished with large blocks of Cornish granite. The upper storey was designed to take eight 64-pound guns with a central magazine area for ammunition. The larger fort at the extreme end of the outer arm is twice the size and was begun in 1861. Being 200 feet in diameter it was a major part of the construction works, 'upon a mass of *pierre perdue*, carefully brought up in layers from the clay bottom, which is about 58 feet below low water mark, to within 20 feet of that level. A ring of masonry, 200 feet in external diameter, and averaging 11 feet in thickness, with radial piers 27 feet in length, is built from 27 feet below to 12 feet above high water mark.'[24] Along with courses of Portland stone and Cornish granite were 'three slabs of Yorkshire landing, very large and thick'. It was May 1868 when it reached clear of high water and it was then handed over to the War Department. The *pierre perdue* was a special foundation material also described in the Committee report in John Coode's specification dated 1861:

> 'No material to be loaded into the wagons except the flint beds and clean rubble, clean quarry chippings, and grit, free from all admixture of earth and soil. The largest stones for this purpose must not exceed two tons, but where stones of this size are sent, there must not be more than one "craned" or heavy stone in each wagon, the remainder of the load in each case to be made up with rubble, spawls, and chippings of all sizes, from stones of 2cwt. each down to fine grit, mixed in such proportions as to make the mass compact and free from interstices. The wagons containing this special foundation material must be sent to the weigh-bridge in separate trains, and marked.'

The larger fort is now known as Chequers Fort. By 1861 a coaling jetty, landing wharf and a huge coal store were nearing completion near the base of the breakwater. The latest hydraulic machinery was installed to aid the loading of coal into ships.

February 1860 saw the formation of the Portland Breakwater Artillery Corps and a meeting of members unanimously proposed that J T Leather should be made Captain with Mr Beaufort and Mr Powel as Lieutenants. The members were mostly young men employed on the works 'and from the spirited manner in which they first came forward, and the zeal since exhibited, little doubt can be entertained of its becoming one of the most effective artillery corps in the county'. J T Leather must have taken this with some diffidence and no doubt acted mainly as a figurehead to get the group off the ground. Two years later, a Captain Browne was chairing a meeting of the Portland Artillery Corps. JTL's attitude to the army was on the whole not enthusiastic. In this connection his grandson by marriage, Sir Desmond

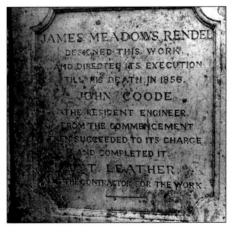

Commemoration Stone records the names of James Rendel, John Coode and John Towlerton Leather

[24] Committee Report on Fortifications 1869.

Morton[25], in a letter about JTL and written in 1967, reminisced: 'One thing I was told, though not in the following brutal words, was that he loathed the Army and soldiers, and was depressed and angry beyond measure when my mother [JTL's daughter Edith] fell in love with my father [Colonel Charles Falkiner Morton]. He would not give his consent to the marriage, whereby my mother, being a very dutiful person, would not marry until after her father's death.' However, when his eldest grandson Gerard entered training for the army in Oxford, he gave a certain amount of friendly encouragement, though he did profess to be rather ignorant about such matters.

In August 1861, Prince Albert and royal party once again visited Portland. It was Prince Albert's final visit before his death later in the year. One advantage of the royal visits is that much more is recorded about the progress of the works, as the occasions were reported in detail in the national press together with illustrations. This time J T Leather is named as one who welcomed the royal party at the breakwater, together with John Coode, E P Smith, and Beaufort etc. Besides Prince Albert there were the Princess Royal, the Prince and Princess Frederick William of Prussia and Prince Arthur. The parties divided. The princesses were taken by train along the breakwater by E P Smith and Beaufort – 'thoroughly amused by the novel mode of conveyance over the Breakwater', while the princes climbed to the fortifications on Verne Hill. The Dorset County Chronicle reports: 'crossing the railway they next entered the great Verne Ditch by the eastern end. This enormous excavation is now nearly finished and as it approaches completion it seems to excite less wonder or surprise in the mind of the casual observer when the space was cut up into a multitude of parts and terraced into graduated steps by the operations of the workmen. For the past three years hundreds of tons of stone have been daily taken from this ditch to the Breakwater.'

The Prince of Wales fixing the last stone of the Portland Breakwater, 29 July 1872. (ILN)

---

[25] In the 1920s Sir Desmond Morton was personal aide to Churchill.

JTL's contract finished at the end of 1866 when, except for the larger fort and finishing touches, the breakwater was more or less complete. The whole of the buildings, offices and plant went to the Admiralty with remaining work still under John Coode. J T Leather's residence at Portland was turned into a hospital for the sick. Details of the cost of the breakwater and forts were outlined in a *Times*[26] article entitled 'The Great Breakwater' where it claimed: 'The money spent upon Portland may fairly be termed a profitable and most worthy investment of our national wealth, …the country has fairly got every iota of advantage that was promised in return for its money.'

John Coode was knighted in March 1872 for the 25 years' work he had carried out at Portland. To mark the completion of the breakwater Edward Albert, Prince of Wales, arrived on 29 July 1872 to lay the finishing stone, complementing the laying of the foundation stone in 1849 by his father, the Prince Consort. There were tremendous celebrations and festivities in both Weymouth and Portland. The new harbour was filled with ships, including fifteen steam war ships, known as broadside ironclads. They were arranged in three columns of five, all with their flags flying.

During the construction of the 1.6 mile (2½ km) breakwater a total of 5,731,376 tons of stone had been quarried and weighed, most of it going to the bottom of the sea

The fleet of Ironclads in Portland Harbour, to welcome the Prince Consort and celebrate the completion of the Portland Breakwater on 29 July 1872. (ILN)

---

[26] *The Times* (December 1862), reprinted in *The Dorset County Chronicle* 18 December 1862

to build up the huge embankment and the foundations of the three forts. It was the making of the biggest deep-water harbour in Great Britain and the cost of just over one million pounds was considered excellent value.

Bridge Builder and Trouble Shooter

John Towlerton Leather becomes so successful and dependable that he is called in to deal with more than one sticky situation. Over the period from 1854-56, while still working on the Portland Breakwater, he contracted for the foundations and masonry work of two iron bridges, one in Inverness and the other at Wisbech in Cambridgeshire. He also took on the strengthening and repair of the banks of the River Nene at Wisbech. A few years later, in an emergency situation, he was asked to construct a dam on the Middle Drain in the Norfolk fenland where a previous one had given way allowing the sea to flood thousands of acres of farmland.

Inverness   Early in February 1854 James Meadows Rendel, engineer of the Portland Breakwater, brought in Contractor Leather – after the failure of two other contractors – to put in the foundations of the new suspension bridge at Inverness. The work was carried out under very difficult circumstances, the story of it going back to the disastrous flood of 1849.

In January of that year strong gales were experienced in northeast Scotland with regular thunderstorms accompanied by heavy rain. Loch Ness had risen fourteen feet above its normal level and the River Ness was in full flood. On 24 February the river was so high that low-lying parts of the town of Inverness were under water. The weekly *Inverness Courier* was being printed in the evening, but before it had been run off, the printing machine was standing in three inches of water, and during the night the Caledonian Canal burst its banks, emptying considerably more water into the river. The combined floodwaters of river and canal surged along the five-mile stretch from Loch Ness to Inverness, submerging one third of the town. The great flood carried away the old stone bridge, together with two new footbridges across to Ness Islands, near the town. The only bridge left was the wooden toll bridge down river, where the modern Waterloo Bridge now stands.

The old seven arch stone bridge, built in 1678, was the main route into the town. This was also a toll bridge, free on Sundays, ensuring that poorer churchgoers on the west bank had no excuse not to attend Sunday service. In the eighteenth century, one of the stone arches on the town side housed a small prison, measuring four yards by three and only six feet high. The door was a hole in the pavement. The collapse of the bridge is graphically described in the *Inverness Courier*:

'The bridge lamps had continued to burn, but all at once the lights went out, a slight groaning sound was heard, the centre arch gave way, and a minute afterwards the whole seven arches at once disappeared beneath the flood, leaving only a portion of the pier and parapet of the arch next Bridge Street, with the lamp attached. The obstruction caused by the fallen materials for a moment forced back the mighty flood. It rose high over the banks, swept up to the houses in Gordon Place, and then as rapidly receded, and the current rushed on, foaming and boiling in frightful waves over the fallen fragments of the bridge.'

Six months later in August of 1849, following a deputation to London by the Inverness Town Council, the government offered £4,000 towards a new bridge, and James Meadows Rendel was asked to design it and decide the best position for it. After trial borings of the riverbed Rendel opted for the site to be where the old stone bridge had stood. He recommended an iron girder bridge at an estimated cost of £16,000 with the alternative of a suspension bridge at £13,500. The trial borings went down forty feet into the riverbed. The first ten feet were sand and gravel, and below this was strong firm clay. A year later, on 31 October 1850, the Chancellor of the Exchequer proposed to advance the whole sum for the bridge, half the amount as a grant, and the rest in the form of a loan born by the four counties of Inverness, Ross, Sutherland and Caithness to be paid back at 6½% over twenty-two years. Detailed plans were received, the estimates now being £20,000 for the girder structure and £18,000 for the suspension bridge.

In January 1851, two years after the flood, the Inverness County finance committee chose to have the cheaper one, the suspension bridge, and on 7 August, the Inverness Bridge Bill passed its third reading in the House of Lords. James Rendel's design was unusual and attractive, with a high tower at the town end in the form of a fine castellated arch and lower pillars at the western end, giving not only a pleasing asymmetry to the bridge but making an impressive and accentuated entry into the city, with the castle in the background on the hill. It was not until the following spring (March 1852) that Messrs Thomas Hutchings and Company were given the contract to build the bridge. They had built the docks at Grimsby and were working on the Morayshire Railway and were well recommended. In March it is reported that workmen had begun removing a group of buildings known as Castle Tolimie at the foot of Bridge Street. A house dated 1678 – the year the old stone bridge was begun – was demolished and said to be one of the most important buildings in the town. A Gaelic bible printed in 1690 was found among the rubble. Six months later, the contractors went bankrupt. They apparently had large contracts for land reclamation in Holland worth half a million pounds.

In March 1853 work was continuing again after the second contractor, Mr Hendrie, was appointed. Workmen had dug down and uncovered an oak foundation beam,

Inverness Suspension Bridge, opened in 1855. In 1939 it was replaced by a wider stone bridge. This old sketch also shows St Columba Church of Scotland, the Castle and the adjoining prison. (Inverness Library)

part of the wooden bridge that straddled the Ness before the erection of the stone one. The beam was a splendid block of oak and beneath it were discovered about a dozen elegant dress pins, each four to seven inches long, 'bright yellow in colour and made of copper and zinc'. In further digging of the foundation of the great tower, a bed of hard clay was met with, 'almost as hard as stone itself'. By August, the *Inverness Courier* reported that the building of the new Ness Bridge was proceeding very slowly:

> 'The contractor, Mr Hendrie, has been working with might and main, and he has lately been in the south obtaining large pumps for emptying the cofferdam. The hard and stony nature of the lower soil, into which the piles had to be driven, and the porous, gravelly nature of the upper stratum, have been the chief difficulties to contend with. The improvements at the western end of Castle Hill had been all but completed. The most marked improvements affected by the Commissioners are enclosing the grounds [of the castle] with a good wall, smoothing the surface of the hill, re-sowing the whole with grass, and planting a row of trees, which will hereafter form a pleasant overhanging screen along the roadside and the bank of the river.'

However, amid much bad management and lack of funds on the part of Mr Hendrie, in January 1854 Inverness Town Council drew up a memorial protesting at the delay on the bridge. One of the magistrates stood and declared: 'Five years have now gone by and not a pillar of this bridge is finished yet; no, nor half a pillar!' Mr Hendrie had also gone bankrupt and all his plant and materials worth several hundred pounds went to the Commissioners.

By early March 1854, James Rendel[27] had 'induced Mr Leather who is executing the Portland Breakwater works for the Lords of the Admiralty, to undertake the completion of the works contracted for by Mr Hendrie, at cost price.' JTL had to travel the 600 miles from Dorset to deal with the situation. He first obtained permission from Colonel Baillie to raise stone from two quarries at Tarradale and Redcastle, nearby on the north side of the Beauly Firth, from where it was brought by barge. The stone is from the middle Old Red Sandstone of the area and an excellent building stone. In writing to the Commissioners[28] Mr Rendel states:

> '…the works are now being proceeded with, in a manner which promises their early completion. The iron-work for the bridge, under contract to Messrs Armstrong of Newcastle upon Tyne, is so nearly completed that it could all be delivered in a month, and I therefore trust that the bridge will be opened to the public by the autumn of this year.
>
> The delays in the completion of the Bridge are mainly attributable to the bankruptcy of the two parties who, in succession, had contracted for the masonry. These parties, at the time they became contractors, were strongly recommended as responsible.'

There was still nearly £12,000 available for the completion of the bridge, a sum James Rendel considered sufficient. There was some discussion about the foundations and the report made by the engineer Mr Joseph Mitchell in his initial trial borings. Mr Mitchell wrote that his report of the four borings was borne out by the excavations. He went on to say that 'delays and great expense have arisen from acting in defiance of the information furnished; by burrowing into the hard 'mountain clay' unnecessarily; and attempting to construct a cofferdam through an almost impenetrable material, which of course broke and destroyed the piles.'

But there were still one or two obstacles that were to dog even the new contractor. On 22 June 1854 about twenty stonemasons working on the bridge went on strike for more pay. They received one guinea a week (21 shillings) but demanded a three-shilling rise. In the autumn it was found that the putting in of the foundations was a more difficult job than expected. Bigger and more costly dams had to be built, and steam engine power had to be provided for pumping the water out of the cofferdams.

[27] 40th Report of the Commissioners for Repair of Roads and Bridges in Scotland, March 1954, letter from James Rendel.
[28] 41st Report of the Commissioners for Repair of Roads and Bridges in Scotland, June 1855, letter from James Rendel.

By the following March (1855) James Rendel was able to report that all the problems had been overcome and that 'had the winter not been so severe, the whole of the work would have been finished by now'. His report continues:

'The works on the west side are all founded and brought to such an advanced state, that they may be completed in a few weeks after the frost is gone, and the masons can resume their labours; whilst in respects of the ironwork, a portion is fixed on the east side, and the whole of it is delivered in Inverness, and the scaffolding is now being erected across the river preparatory to the fixing in place the main suspension chains and roadway.'

Inverness Suspension Bridge designed by J M Rendel and erected by J T Leather in 1855 after the failure of two other contractors. (Highland Photographic Archive)

The accounts show a payment of £11,109 to Mr Leather, with a note to say the bridge will be open next month (April). In fact the bridge was completed in August and not opened until September, 1855. The final delay had been in the delivery of the wooden blocks for the road surface – they were lying at Leith waiting for shipment. The end grain wooden pavement blocks, set in coal-tar were similar to their successful use on the High Level Bridge at Newcastle. Strong criticism ended with the remark, 'Every step with regard to this bridge seems doomed to misfortune or mismanagement!'

On 23 August 1855 the new Inverness suspension bridge was opened to traffic. The *Courier* describes the event; 'Carriages and foot passengers have today for the first time had a free passage across it, and throughout this week Mr Rendel had endeavoured to give every accommodation in his power to vehicles having occasion to cross the river. Now that the bridge is finished, we must do it the justice to say that it is by far the finest construction of the kind in the north of Scotland. The span is 225 feet, and the solidity and finish of the work are spoken of by all competent judges as unequalled in the Highlands, and unsurpassed anywhere.' The final cost was £25,365.

The bridge served the town well until the use of heavy motorised traffic became too much for it. In the mid-nineteen-thirties the engineer and local Member of Parliament, Sir Murdoch MacDonald, made a report on the bridge urging immediate repairs and that a speed limit of ten miles per hour be imposed. He also advised that a new bridge should replace the suspension bridge. For a few years a man with a red flag kept the traffic in check. In 1939, the decision was taken for a new bridge to be constructed of Shap granite and, in the mean time, a temporary wooden bridge was placed across the Ness for use while the new one was being built.

Wisbech There had always been a need for hydraulic engineers in the Cambridgeshire and Norfolk Fens where they drain to the Wash and the North Sea. The low lying

The Old Stone Bridge at Wisbech in about 1854. The bridge had a 74-foot span, was built in 1758 and much loved by local people (Samuel Smith Collection, Wisbech and Fenland Museum)

land is constantly under threat of flooding by the sea, where drainage schemes incorporate sluices that allow water out at low tide but stop the sea from entering as the tide rises. The three rivers that drain into the Wash are the Welland, the Nene and the Great Ouse. In 1836, civil engineer John Rennie[29] reported on the River Nene where it flows through the market town and port of Wisbech. His recommendations included the removal of the stone bridge at Wisbech with a view to widening the river channel in order to lessen the tidal scour along the banks. He also advocated a wet dock and a lock, up-river above Bevis Hall, to enable vessels drawing seven feet of water to reach Peterborough. In 1840 he amended his plan to include a new 1½-mile channel, and make the narrow, winding channel through the town into a dock. There was no lack of advice, for in 1848 the engineer Robert Stephenson made a report on more or less the same lines.

Eventually, James Meadows Rendel was called in as engineer and in 1851 the Nene Valley Commissioners applied to Parliament for powers to carry out the River Nene Improvements. James Rendel had designed several chain ferries operated by steam power and executed docks at Grimsby, Leith and at Garston on the Mersey. The Admiralty employed him for work on the harbour at Holyhead. He also worked on many bridges and harbours in Britain and around the world. One of his last achievements before his death at the age of 57 was a design for the suspension bridge across St James Park in London.

Details of the Nene plan included strengthening the riverbanks and deepening the channel to a uniform depth. At Wisbech extensive wharfage was to be provided with a new bridge, at an estimate of £150,000. The Wisbech Mayor and Corporation were staggered at the high cost which was to include a contribution of £40,000 from Wisbech, and decided to oppose the scheme. However, civil engineer George Hurwood was sent from the Admiralty to explain and promote the scheme. So, with trusted engineers John Rennie, Robert Stephenson and James Rendel behind it, Wisbech Corporation finally accepted and the Act was passed in 1852. In November of that year there was a further collapse of the river wall in the town of Wisbech. Heavy rains had fallen and surging waters cut through the narrow channel destroying sixty feet of the bank opposite the town hall, while part of the roadway on the Nene Quay gave way at the back of the Rose and Crown Hotel. On the other side of the river, the premises of the King's Head Inn were undermined until a small building at its rear fell bodily into the water. Mr William Adams, the borough surveyor took action and tipped 200 tons of chalk into the river near the Stone Bridge to keep it safe while men were busy filling the holes in the bank, which continued to appear.

---

[29] History of Wisbech and Neighbourhood – during the past fifty years 1848-1898 by F J Gardiner, Editor of the Isle of Ely and Wisbech Advertiser (published 1898, Wisbech Advertiser). Succeeding historical notes from the same source.

River Nene at Wisbech showing all the river traffic at low tide. (Samuel Smith Collection, Wisbech and Fenland Museum)

J T Leather was finally approached and his tender accepted. The Admiralty gave its sanction in December 1853, and work commenced in January 1854. The Admiralty was particularly interested in this scheme as it would give navy ships, if threatened, a retreat as far up river as Peterborough. The new bridge at Wisbech would, therefore, have to be one that could be opened to river traffic. The total cost of the Nene river works, that of strengthening and repairing the banks of the River Nene between Peterborough and Wisbech and the deepening of Wisbech harbour, finally came to £124,800, the whole to be completed in four years.

Applications were made to Parliament for loans, but with the Admiralty insisting on a more expensive opening bridge, the amount that Wisbech had to contribute was increased by a further £12,000. This was the last straw. The mayor and members of the Corporation had personally advanced sums of up to £1,000 and they could not raise any more. The full scheme was never completed, but some progress was made, mainly in Wisbech. Wooden piling was put into place along riverbank at Nene Parade and along the Nene Quay, with piling machines blocking the quay for a time. A dredging machine brought material from the riverbed and dumped it behind the new piling. Apart from these essential repairs there was not a great deal to show for ten months work before the project was abandoned in November 1854, that is, except for the Wisbech Bridge.

In preparation for the new swing bridge over the River Nene, a temporary wooden one was completed opposite the White Hart Hotel, in November 1854. A large space had to be cleared for the swing end of the new bridge and the fine building of the Butter Cross, purchased for £3,500 by the Commissioners, was demolished as well as the old houses on the Cornhill, where the post office had been. The Green Dragon Inn was also removed to enlarge the approaches. A special jury at the Rose and Crown assessed the value of John Lawson's granary at £2,200 after a claim of £4,500, and the nervous Corporation applied (and succeeded) – at a cost of over £1,000 – for Parliamentary powers to keep the rate below 10p in the pound. The loss of the Butter Cross was damaging for the town, a market place for the sale of poultry, butter and eggs, was replaced by an unsatisfactory portable framework on Market Hill, much to the detriment of trade.

The Butter Cross, Wisbech, built 1804. This fine building had to be demolished along with some old houses on the Cornhill to make way for the new Swing Bridge. (from History of Wisbech)

What were once gently sloping sides of the River Nene had, over the previous 100 years, been built up within the town and replaced by vertical wharves so that ships could readily come alongside and discharge or load their cargo. Trade had improved although the channel through the town was narrow. Then, in 1836, the outfall of the river had been opened up after which the tidal range at Wisbech increased from a mere four feet to twelve feet or more. This had the welcome effect of scouring the bed of the river, deepening it and generally improving navigation. At the same time the scouring of the banks was gradually having a cumulative effect – they were

Nene Quay Wisbech about 1856. The narrow channel led to increased erosion to the steep banks from the strong flow of the tide. (Samuel Smith Collection Wisbech and Fenland Museum)

Old Wisbech Bridge in 1855 being demolished to make way for the new iron swing bridge. (Samuel Smith Collection, Wisbech and Fenland Museum)

beginning to give way. The main reason for removing the beautiful stone bridge was to widen the channel through the town and therefore lessen the scour of the tidal flow. The town did not want the extra expense of a swing bridge, which appeared unnecessary. In an effort to persuade the admiralty to let them have a fixed bridge, in 1852, a survey was carried out to show how much traffic made use of the bridge. This makes interesting reading and shows how busy a market centre the town had become. On a Saturday in May between 5.00am and 6.00pm there were some 21,000 passengers, 530 carriages, 700 horses, and over 1,000 sheep, pigs and other animals. Weekdays showed roughly half these figures, while Sunday was a particularly quiet day for animals.

In March 1855 the fine stone bridge which had graced the town for ninety-seven years, was dismantled. The work was under the direction of Mr Penistone, resident engineer. The bridge had an elliptical arch with a 74 feet span and was built in 1758 at a cost of £2,250. It had been compared to the Rialto Bridge in Venice. However, though an attractive piece of architecture with stone balustrade, the bridge was steep and very narrow. 'Heavily laden waggons coming down into Bridge Street had been known to be precipitated into the glass windows of Mr Smith Flanders' shop, and when the heavy caravans of Wombwell's Menagerie tried to cross, the extra wide van carrying the elephant had to be jacked up so that the wheels ran on the pavement on each side of the roadway.

There was obviously a great liking for the old bridge and general dismay in the town for its demolition. No doubt J T Leather sensed that he was destroying a much-loved feature of Wisbech and in October 1855, he presented the foundation stone of the old bridge to the museum. A plate on the stone, inscribed in Latin, stated: *Ex Ligneo Surrexit Lapideus. A.D. 1758. Esto perpetuus*, which put into English would read, 'After a wooden (bridge) there has arisen a stone one, AD 1758. May it last for ever.' But it did not last 100 years. Contractor Leather's presentation plate is still to be seen in Wisbech Museum.

> **Presented to**
> **THE WISBECH MUSEUM BY**
> **John Towlerton Leather (Esquire)**
> **of Leventhorpe Hall near Leeds**
> **CONTRACTOR**
> **for the River Nene Improvements**
> **OCTOBER A.D. 1855**

Presentation plate presented by JTL to Wisbech Museum along with the foundation stone of the old stone bridge.

James Meadows Rendel FRS was the designer of the new iron swing bridge. It was to be 156 feet long, 40 feet wide and the sides were 8 feet high. It balanced on a pivot one third of the way along its length to allow it to open (52 feet from the land end and 104 feet from the longer end). The shorter third was provided with rollers, with extra weight (to about 120 tons) to maintain its balance. At the pivot, the hydraulic lift consisted of a of a large piston, tightly fitted into a cylinder, into which water was pumped when the bridge was opened, thus bearing the weight of the structure and enabling it to be turned easily. When the bridge was closed, the water was let out and the bridge rested on its normal bearings. A tower, built of corrugated iron, was to house the pump and lifting gear. The ironwork of the bridge was by Armstrong and Co. of Elswick Works, Newcastle upon Tyne, and the same contractors as for the Inverness Suspension Bridge.

On 11 April 1856 the foundation stone of the new iron bridge was laid by the mayor of Wisbech, Mr J E Fraser, who was presented with a silver trowel for the purpose. The ceremony was carried out at four o'clock in the afternoon and, two hours later at the Rose and Crown Hotel, John Towlerton Leather, James Meadows Rendel

Wisbech Iron Bridge c1859. Designed by J M Rendell and constructed by J T Leather, the bridge swung open only once in its existence. The tower held the complex pulley arrangement enabling the bridge to swing. It was demolished in 1930 and replaced by a reinforced concrete bridge. (Samuel Smith Collection Wisbech and Fenland Museum)

and resident engineer Mr Borthwick all gathered for a dinner, with the Marquis of Huntly, chairman of the Nene Valley Commissioners, presiding. Also present were members of the council and other gentlemen of the town. Tickets were twelve shillings each. Here it was stated that, when the bridge was completed, it would be the biggest opening bridge in the world.

In November of that year came the untimely death of engineer James Meadows Rendel. He was replaced by John Fowler who addressed the Commissioners of the Nene Valley Drainage pointing out that some of their works were in a dangerous condition owing to excessive scour along the channel. As a temporary expedient John Fowler placed a submerged weir across the river with self-acting gates. This contraption at Wisbech prevented ships from coming into the town and resulted in many problems. After some delay and further arguments about costs, the Wisbech council asked for the bridge to be completed as soon as possible.

A year later, in November 1857, before the mayor formally opened it, the bridge had a trial opening of its own when it was swung for the first time – and for the last time in its history! Mr F J Gardiner, who was on the bridge when it opened, describes it in his book *The History of Wisbech*. It took place at six o'clock in the morning with the mayor and a few members of the Corporation there to witness the big event.

> 'Five or six men were employed in the tower to work the machinery, which, by means of hydraulic pressure, raised the accumulator, a perpendicular cylinder, loaded to the extent of forty tons. By turning a tap, the pressure was communicated to the cylinder upon which the bridge revolved, and the weight of the accumulator moving the chains, swung the ponderous mass on its pivot to the piling on the south side, making a clear opening up and down the river. The steady motion of the bridge as it swung round to the south side showed that the machinery was equal to the strain, and it remained in its open position until four o'clock in the afternoon when it was again put across.'

A few days later on 9 November 1857, the new Wisbech Bridge, at a cost of £15,000, was opened by Mayor Steed Watson, who was driven over it in his carriage to the town hall, where he was re-elected mayor. The first person to drive himself over was Mr Richard Young and the first to go over on horseback was Mr Robert Dawbarn. These gentlemen were two other candidates for mayor of the town.

The bridge never needed to be opened again and the machinery fell into disuse and became rusty and unreliable. Many years later, the Admiralty conceded that the bridge should become a fixed one. The tower was removed and the bridge shortened by removing the third of it that balanced the bridge proper. The result was a great improvement in the approaches. But it was not until 1930, after standing for seventy-three years, that the iron bridge was dismantled and the present reinforced concrete bridge built to replace it. The old iron bridge had received much criticism: 'a hideous structure', 'an eyesore to the town', 'its inconvenience and ugliness', etc. The sides were certainly too high, and traffic coming across could not see what was approaching round the corner. Most people in the town were glad to see the end of it!

The Middle Level Drain This broad aqueduct runs across the low lying land of the Fens, and enters the River Great Ouse about four miles before it reaches the sea at Kings Lynn. The scheme, to improve navigation and drainage, was devised by civil engineer James Walker – President of the Institution of Civil Engineers between 1835 and 1845 – and sanctioned by Act of Parliament in 1844. The twelve-mile long new cut was constructed to connect the old Sixteen Foot Drain near Outwell with the River Ouse at Wiggenhall St German, with a bottom width of forty-eight feet and gently sloping sides. There were other drains built under the same Act and many, including the Sixteen Foot Drain, were to be widened, deepened and altered. On the Middle Level Drain a sluice was built at Outwell and, at the lower end at St German's, close to the River Ouse, the Main Outfall Sluice was constructed. It was completed in 1847 and this was the sluice that failed only fifteen years later, in May 1862. F J Gardiner gives a description of it[30]:

> 'This was a substantial structure consisting of a bridge of three arches, each of twenty feet span, resting on piers of great solidity, and flanked on both sides with wide spreading wings or walls to support the adjacent banks. Each of the arches enclosed a pair of very strong oaken doors or gates opening towards the river, and constituting self-acting sluices which allowed the waters to pass outwards, but prevented tidal waters from entering the drain. The cost of Mr Walker's scheme (including nearly £30,000 for the sluice) was about £650,000.'

The Middle Level Drain was further improved and completed to the full depth of seventeen feet in 1857. On 4 May 1862, the St German's Outfall Sluice, at the point where the aqueduct meets the Great Ouse, gave way and tidal waters rushed up the channel to a distance of twenty miles, eventually breaching the sides and flooding nine square miles of land on the north side of the channel.

A few weeks before the sluice collapsed John Hawkshaw, (later Sir John, and President of the Institution of Civil Engineers) was in the area on other business but visited and made a sketch of the sluice. He commented that he admired the design and fabric of the sluice, though he had no suspicion that it was in any danger.

The floods of 4 May 1862 produced an emergency situation. The foundations of the sluice were undermined and two of the three arches fell. A gap developed and the channel seemed to double in width, lighters sank and one of the bridges was swept away. Thousands of sandbags were used to try and stem the tide. A week later the west bank of the drain gave way four miles further up and a gap 150 feet wide allowed seawater to pour unhindered onto thousands of acres of quality farmland.

---

[30] *History of Wisbech and Neighbourhood – during the past fifty years 1848-1898* by F J Gardiner, Editor of the Isle of Ely and Wisbech Advertiser (pub. Wisbech Advertiser, 1898).

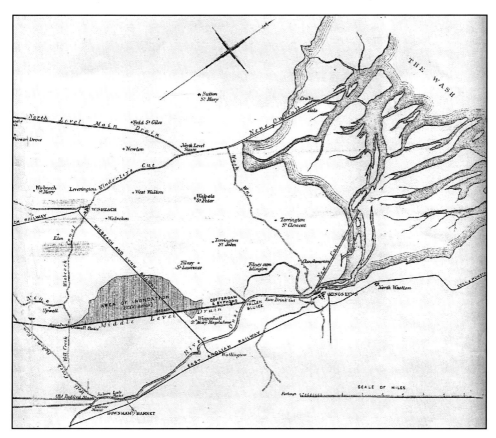

Map of the Fens around Wisbech and Kings Lynn showing the flooded area and the position of the coffer dam. (Proceedings of ICE Vol 22, 1862-63)

There was enough warning to get farmers and livestock away, but buildings and crops were ruined and under several feet of water. The Wisbech and Kings Lynn railway line was inundated and telegraph poles were carried away. F J Gardiner, later editor of the *Isle of Ely and Wisbech Advertiser* remembers sailing a boat over the flooded fenland, 'and watching a train trying to force its way over the flooded line, in an attempt that failed because the fires were put out by the depth of water'. The scene was so unique that special trains were run from London to see the Great Fen Flood. Another writer, J M Heathcote also writes about it:

> 'I stood on the bank close by a breach many yards wide which admitted a fresh stream of tidal water at every return of the tide up the cut. A vast extent of water covered the whole surface of the district before us. Nothing was to be seen but water, except that an occasional farmhouse and willows, a few posts and the tops of hedges just appeared above what is now a lake. Here and there

was a boat going to or returning from an inundated residence to save the wreck of furniture.'

Civil Engineer John Hawkshaw[31] was sent for to deal with the disastrous flooding and 'to do whatever was necessary to shut out the tidal waters, regardless of expense'.

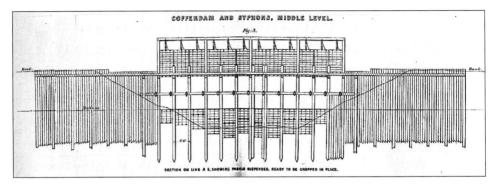

Drawing by Engineer John Hawkshaw of the cofferdam showing the 7 inch thick oak sliding panels suspended and ready to be dropped into place. When the panels were lowered into position by a pulley system, 800 men were employed with wheelbarrows to shore up the structure with clay, gravel and chalk against the incoming tide. (Proceedings of ICE Vol 22, 1862-63)

He visited the scene of the disaster and soon designed a new cofferdam with siphons running over the top. He secured the services of John Towlerton Leather – in a further break from the Portland Breakwater – to carry out the building work. Sir John notes that Mr J T Leather 'was fitted, from his extensive experience, to carry out my plans, which he did with much vigour and judgement. In this he was ably assisted by Mr E P Smith'. Mr Alexander G Linn was appointed resident engineer. Because of the emergency, no contract was drawn up for either the Middle Level cofferdam nor for the Inverness suspension bridge and, as J T Leather's obituary[32] states, 'the fact that they were entrusted to Mr Leather, by their respective engineers under these circumstances, is a striking testimony, therefore, to the confidence reposed both in his skill, his energy, and his integrity.

The sea had to be closed off by means of a permanent cofferdam of pile-work across

[31] John Hawkshaw, FRS, '*Account of the Cofferdam, the Siphons and Other Works, Constructed in Consequence of the Failure of the St German's Sluice of the Middle Level Drainage*' in Minutes of the Proceedings of the Institution of Civil Engineers, 1862, Vol. 22, pp 497-511.

[32] Obituary in Minutes of the Proceedings of the Institution of Civil Engineers, Vol. 83, pp 433-436, 1885/6.

the drain. The site was half a mile from the confluence with the River Ouse. This was a very delicate job as the tide came in at a speed of about 5mph and the sides of the drain were only of soft material and easily eroded. The breach higher up was left until the cofferdam was in place to minimise the rush of tidal water. The final closing of the dam had to be put into place during the few hours of low tide, and ready to meet and hold the incoming tide. The utmost care was essential.

The original intention was to make use of a timber road bridge that crossed the drain about 1,000 yards upstream and to use it as staging from which to drive in the piles. But they had hardly got started when a barge broke loose and hit the bridge with such force that it destroyed it.

Middle Level Drain. Construction of the cofferdam. First, temporary piles were sunk into the ground and a platform erected to form staging for the pile-driving engines. Two rows of piles were then put across the Drain, 25 feet apart. (Wisbech and Fenland Museum)

The new site was 120 yards below this bridge and work began on the 16 May 1862. First, temporary piles were sunk into the ground and a platform erected on them to form a staging for the pile-driving engines. Two rows of piles were put across the

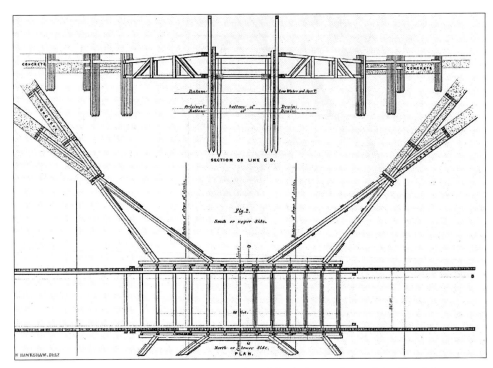

Section and Plan of the cofferdam at Middle Level Drain by engineer John Hawkshaw. (Proceedings ICE Vol 22, 1862-63)

Middle Drain in 1998 showing not a vestige of the coffer dam erected in 1862, the site being about 110m along from this bridge.

drain, twenty-five feet apart. The piles were at intervals of seven feet six inches extending diagonally down the banks with grooves for sliding panels. These panels were made of seven-inch thick oak timbers and suspended on a frame so that they could be lowered (or raised by a pulley system). Once the piles were in place, the rush of water increased to 8 or 9 mph which started to produce a serious scouring of the bed.

The first lowering of the panels was a failure as three of the twin piles fractured when the tidal water increased to a height of eight feet above that on the landward side. On 19 June 1862, only six weeks after the old sluice had given way, a second attempt was made which was a complete success. Sacks of gravel and clay were used to infill the dam. There were as many as 800 men employed and ready at a moment's notice to place 3,000 yards of clay and several hundred sacks of gravel and chalk rock into place behind the lowered panels. Several pathways for wheelbarrows and

The present day dam that operates the Middle Level Drain was built in 1934.

wagon roads were improvised to allow maximum speed. 'And so perfect were the arrangements that the raising of the dam inside was kept in advance of the rising tide, and before high water the operation was completed. The contrast between the rush of water before, and the calm after the operation was remarkable.'

Additional piles were put in to strengthen the existing ones. Then, sixteen cast iron siphon pipes, three foot six inches in diameter, were laid over the cofferdam to form a permanent sluice, with valves automatically allowing water out at low tide, and preventing seawater coming in as the tide rose. The siphons were put into action by exhausting the air from the inside with the use of an air pump worked by a steam engine. The siphons were cast by Cochrane and Co of Woodside Ironworks, Dudley,

Staffordshire, the total weight of all sixteen being over 600 tons. Total materials used in building the cofferdam amounted to 90,000 cubic feet of timber, 75 tons of iron, 430 casks of cement, 2,500 tons of broken chalk and 36,000 sacks.

The breach in the bank higher up the drain was then closed, a clay bank being built upon a stone foundation, and the rest of the banks put into good repair. The dam and siphons worked well but, in spite of its substantial size, only lasted another nine years before another serious flood in 1871 completely undermined the whole system. The dam and siphons were replaced by the New Outfall Sluice built in 1874, also under the direction of Sir John Hawkshaw. The contractor was William Webster. Today there is not a bump in the ground to suggest where any of the three sluices were, and the present one, built in 1934, is a very large and impressive piece of engineering with huge steel gates.

The Great Sheffield Flood

By 1864 John Towlerton Leather could look back on a successful career of 35 years. There had been no failures, he had a reputation for fair dealing and dependability, and the monumental Portland Breakwater and other works had made him widely known and trusted. However, early in that year there was a major tragedy which haunted J T Leather for the rest of his life.

It wasn't just a tragedy for our engineer but for the whole nation, and especially for the people of Sheffield. It was the worst disaster of its kind in British history.

On a dark and wet March night Sheffield Waterworks highest dam collapsed, causing what became known as the Great Sheffield Flood. After heavy rain the reservoir behind the dam had reached its highest point, yet the embankment still looked solid. It suddenly gave way towards midnight sending a wall of water shooting all the way along a narrow valley fifteen miles towards Sheffield. Of all the engineering accidents and disasters of the nineteenth century this was the worst in the destruction of life and property. It challenged the confidence that man can control nature, and it was also, at the time, unexplained.

The final two reservoirs for Sheffield Waterworks that JTL designed were the Dale Dyke and Agden dams, passed by Act of Parliament in 1852. The two were to be large service reservoirs, each embankment 95 feet in height. Only one dam exceeding this height had so far been built in Britain, designed by J F Bateman at Torside, Glossop, on the other side of the Pennines with a crest 100 feet above the valley floor. Dale Dyke was at the upper end of the River Loxley, and Agden on a tributary a mile to the north. They were both large undertakings, but it was Dale Dyke which failed.

In planning the dams, JTL would have had in mind the terrible accident of February 1852 when the Bilberry dam in the Holmfirth valley near Huddersfield failed, and 89 people died. George Leather (JTL's uncle) had been the chief engineer and, for him, it was the end of a brilliant career. However, the fault was not entirely his. In the lead up to the building of the Bilberry dam, the Commissioners, trying to save money, did not engage an engineer to advise them on siting the dam. Ignorance and lack of experience led them to choose a site without making exploratory pits or trenches, purely from a consideration of the shape and depth of the valley. A year after the

Act of Parliament, the Commissioners invited George Leather to 'undertake the management' of the reservoir and 'you would only be required to come over now and again'. George Leather replied that 'plans and specifications should be prepared and the work properly laid out, and then to employ practical men to be constantly on the spot'. The reason for the failure appears to have been a combination of George Leather's instructions not being carried out and his fees not being paid by the Commissioners. He apparently therefore 'walked away from' the project.

At Dale Dyke JTL's detailed preliminary survey of the underlying geology mapped the position of springs and the lie of the strata, and ascertained the amount and depth of clay, shale and sandstone that could be used in the construction. He designed the embankment to ensure a perfect seal that would reach down well below the floor of the valley. The Dale Dyke dam was to be sited at the head of the Loxley valley, just above the hamlet of Bradfield and fifteen miles west of Sheffield. Trial borings began, which showed the strata to be disturbed where an old landslip had brought material down from the valley side. The line of the dam was therefore moved 150 yards upstream and, in the second plan, a curve was introduced to its south end. Work started on this mammoth project on 1 January 1859.

A year or so later, in the spring of 1860, JTL reported to the Sheffield Water Committee:

> The works of the Dale Dyke have been retarded in some degree, in consequence of the difficulties experienced in arriving at a satisfactory foundation in the middle of the valley, for the puddle wall, which difficulties have been enhanced by the severity of the past winter. There is now, however, every prospect of a favourable change and it is hoped that the works will be vigorously prosecuted during the ensuing season.

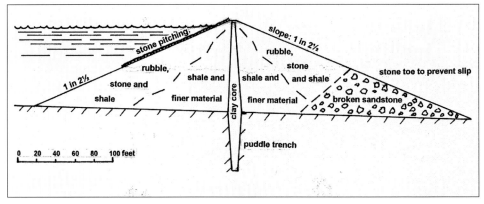

Section through the Dale Dyke Dam drawn from evidence given by J T Leather and J Gunson at the Inquest. (after Binnie)

JTL modified the plan of the trench for the core wall, deepening it in order to reach solid rock and a watertight base. Its maximum depth was *sixty feet* below the valley floor. This part of the work was finished by mid-1861. The construction of the embankment began that autumn. Cast iron pipes were taken beneath the embankment. To avoid fracturing, the pipe trench dipped at the centre but still crossed puddle core thirty feet above its base.[33]. Settlement of the wet puddle clay could thus lead to possible fracturing of the pipes here. The pipes were nine feet long and the puddle trench at this point about 10 or 12 feet across. Along the rest of their length the pipes were laid in a trench and surrounded by an eighteen inch thick layer of puddle with outlet valves at the downstream end. The core of puddle clay within the barrier was relatively narrow, only 4 feet wide at the top of the embankment and 16 feet at ground level. The overflow weir was excavated in solid ground and had a 65 foot long curved sill, 5 feet below the top of the dam. In his report to the Committee in April 1863 John Towlerton writes:

> I am happy to report that notwithstanding the more than ordinary difficulties which have been encountered in the construction of the Dale Dyke reservoir, the embankment is now so far completed as to be ready for the reception of the Water, and the Waste Weir, which is not quite finished, may be soon so in the course of a few weeks from the present time, and the Works throughout are well and substantially executed.

In June 1863, the reservoir first began to fill when heavy rain flooded into it from the diversion channel. It was allowed to fill over the next months and by Thursday 10 March 1864 the water level was reported to be only two feet below the crest of the weir and still rising due to heavy rain in the Pennines.

John Gunson, resident engineer and responsible for the dam's construction' lived in the city next to the water company's office on Division Street. On Friday morning 11 March 1864 he read Vice Admiral Fitzroy's forecast of an impending westerly gale in the daily newspaper. Robert Fitzroy, who in his younger days had sailed with Charles Darwin on the Beagle, was a Fellow of the Royal Society and a former Governor of New Zealand; and was well known for the storm warnings he gave from the meteorological department which he had founded. John Gunson took note of the gale warning and decided to visit Dale Dyke embankment in the afternoon to see how it was standing up to the high water level. He travelled with his horse and gig up to Bradfield as he had on so many occasions. He stood at the end of the dam and looked along its 420 yard length – the dam was 'straight as a die'. He did not cross the top because of the spray. He was satisfied that all was well and, about 4 o'clock, returned to his home in Sheffield.

---

[33] Iain Moffat, Professorial Fellow in Dam Engineering adds that it was 'a very dangerous feature of the design, and that JTL allowed Gunson to modify these on his own initiative'

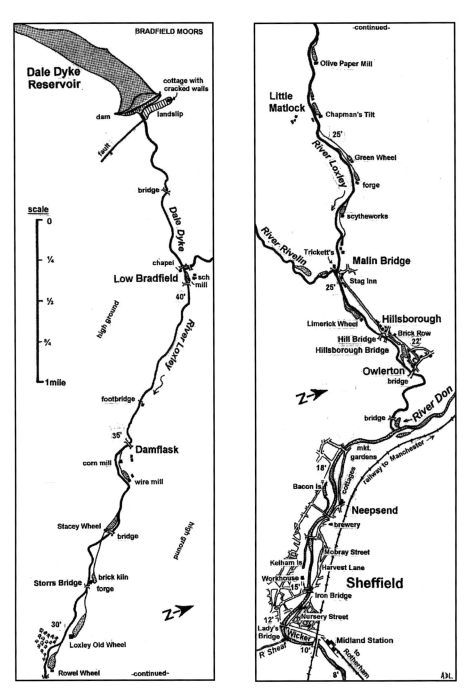

Map showing the Loxley Valley and localities along the trail of destruction with estimated depth of floodwater in feet.

At 5.30pm William Horsefield, who had been working with others on the final part of the weir, was crossing the embankment to his home. As there was a strong wind blowing down the reservoir creating spray over the dam, he decided to walk just below the crest where it was more sheltered, and here he saw a narrow vertical crack in the ground, parallel to the top of the dam – rather like one caused by frost he thought. He decided to tell a fellow workman and a local farmer. They alerted Fountain, one of the contractors, and several others. It was beginning to get dark

The breach from the inside (from Sheffield Flood by Samuel Harrison, 1864)

and lanterns were lit to re-examine the crack. Fountain was alarmed and decided to send his son Stevenson on horseback to Sheffield to recall John Gunson, while workmen opened the valves to let the water through the pipes and relieve some of the pressure. The lad galloped so fast that the saddle strap snapped and he had to stop to repair it at the Barrel Inn, Damflask. It was here people began to learn that the dam was unsafe.

At 10pm John Gunson and Craven, another contractor, arrived by gig. They looked at the crack, now wide enough to fit a man's hand, and Gunson ordered the top stones of the weir to be blasted away to let out more water. They soon realised the seriousness

W Nicholson's impression of the bursting of Dale Dyke Dam (Sheffield Libraries)

of the situation and sent men to warn people who lived below the dam in Bradfield and Damflask. Drills and gunpowder were sent for, but the charge did not go off immediately. Gunson went back to the crack. Water came right over the top of the dam, and ran down the slope to his feet and into the crack. He went down to the base of the dam to see how much water was in the by-wash. Men shouted to him to get back up the slope. Soon after 11.30pm John Gunson watched in astonishment as he saw an opening appear along the centre of the dam about thirty yards long with water streaming down the embankment. A few minutes later the ground shook, there was a terrific surge, the middle of the dam collapsed and, with tremendous force and speed, millions of gallons of water and hundreds of tons of mud went hurtling and thundering down the Loxley valley towards Sheffield. About the same time the charge went off on the weir.

The trail of devastation was absolutely terrible. A thirty foot high wave, travelling at about twenty miles an hour, carried everything before it: bridges, farmhouses, cottages, whole terraces of houses, workshops, mills, forges and factories, all overwhelmed and demolished within minutes. Whole families were swept away, and 4,000 homes flooded. Nearly 250 people lost their lives. It was the worst disaster of the Victorian period.

Being near to midnight, most people were in bed and had little time to escape. About a mile below the dam in Low Bradfield, William Ibbotson had been alerted and banged on doors shouting, 'The flood is coming! Run for your lives!' The five or six families in their night clothes hurried up the dark hillside in the cold March air. Mr Nicholls, the village schoolmaster ran back for his overcoat – to the horror of his wife[34]. He managed to get back up the slope as, a second later a great wall of floodwater came roaring and foaming through the hamlet. Their homes and the school, which had recently been rebuilt to take eighty children, were completely demolished. Bradfield corn mill, a robust three storey stone building, was covered to the roof. It then collapsed and completely disappeared, even the huge grindstone vanished. Thirty of the people of Low Bradfield escaped and spent the night in the house of the miller, Joseph Ibbotson.

Thomas Chapman's house at Little Matlock. (Sheffield Libraries)

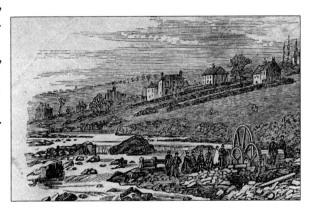

Wisewood Scythe Works at Rowel Bridge just below Little Matlock had only its flywheel jutting out of the mud. (from Sheffield Flood by Samuel Harrison, 1864)

At Damflask, which had also received some warning, there were miraculous escapes though an elderly man who was a worker at the Agden dam, known as 'Sheffield Harry' took no heed of the warnings and was swept away. Four men, working a night shift, were drowned in the wire mill. The eighteen foot boiler from the mill was deposited in the riverbed a quarter of a mile downstream.

---

[34] Samuel Harrison, *A Complete History of the Great Flood at Sheffield (Sheffield Times, 1864)*

Along the four miles from Low Bradfield to Malin Bridge there was a series of twenty-one mills and forges, many of which used tilt hammers or grindstones, each with its mill dam, water conduit and wooden water wheel, close to the river. Never relenting, the floodwater licked up each mill pond one after the other and nothing was spared. A brick kiln at Storrs Bridge was completely washed away and the forge at Loxley Old Wheel was badly damaged.

At Rowel Bridge large quantities of paper were washed away from Olive paper mill, and the Wisewood scytheworks was completely gutted, except for the large fly- and cog-wheels that, next morning stood proud like some industrial sculpture. A rock dropped by the current was estimated to weigh twenty tons.

Malin Bridge (pron. 'male-in') was the first village of any size, situated five and a half miles from the dam, where the River Rivelin joins the Loxley. Here there was no warning. Of the 600 inhabitants, 100 perished and twenty three entire families, except for three individuals, lost their lives. On a shoulder of land between the two rivers was the Trickett's fine farmhouse where ten people lived. None of them survived and, next day, Mrs Trickett's body was found eight miles away in Rotherham. Fourteen milking cows were also carried away. Today there is a garage on this spot and across the river is the old corn mill.

Five miles below the burst at Malin Bridge, the front was torn out of Cleakum Inn and George Bisby, his wife and five children were drowned. (from Sheffield Flood by Samuel Harrison)

The front of Cleakum Inn was torn out and two bridges at Malin Bridge were washed away and whole rows of cottages completely demolished. High on the valley side, tree trunks were jammed forty feet above river level.

As far as Malin Bridge, the raging floodwater had been closely confined by the steep, narrow valley that funnelled it with increasing depth and fury, but below Malin Bridge the valley opens out through Owlerton and Hillsborough (more recently the scene of another disaster at the Sheffield Wednesday football ground). In this stretch there were 250 houses, fifty of which were left in ruins.

The roaring and turbulent water – the noise was described by one as 'a thousand steam engines letting off steam' and by another as 'hissing thunder' – was now only two miles from the centre of Sheffield, but still had the power to demolish factories and houses. With it were carried along many trees, for the Loxley valley was well wooded. There were bodies of cattle, pigs and horses, lighter bits of machinery, parts of the roofs of houses, bits of broken furniture and vast amounts of mud and stones.

It was after midnight when the floodwaters invaded Owlerton where the River Loxley joins the Don. The silver rolling mill and paper mill were both devastated. Large quantities of silver were washed away and four men and a boy ran to safety.

The flood continued to cause havoc to life and property as it entered the lower part of Sheffield itself. The scene of devastation in the area of Neepsend Lane was almost total. Small one-storey cottages in the market gardens near the river were hardest hit. Whole families – five Pettys, four Websters, five Midwoods and eight Gannons – all lost their lives.

In the wider valley, the water was less deep but affected property over a wider area. The gasworks was severely damaged, as were the tanneries. Harvest Lane, Mobray Street, Bacon Island and Kelham Island were some of the areas badly affected. Bacon Island was completely inundated where all nine of the Sharman family were rescued by PC John Thorpe who was commended for his act of bravery, as were fifty other officers and constables for what they did that night.

Hill Bridge at Hillsborough was almost totally destroyed. (Sheffield Libraries)

Near the river, Waterloo Houses consisted of two rows of terrace houses. One of these was completely stripped of the front wall exposing all the interior rooms, both upstairs and downstairs. Most of the occupants escaped by retreating to their back bedrooms as the flood only just reached the first floor.

Several steelworks in Green Lane were badly damaged. There were a considerable number of poor houses in this area and, as the flood came, the pressure of water on the doors prevented people from opening them, so they retreated upstairs where they were safe, though some who slept on the ground floor lost their lives. Many of the biggest of the Sheffield steelworks including Spear and Jackson, Thomas Firth, John Brown, Vickers, Cammel and Jessop, escaped the worst of the flood.

At Kelham Island the rolling mills were flooded and workmen escaped to the roof, where one man saw his own bed float into the works. It had travelled two and a half miles from Malin Bridge where his wife, who had been sleeping on it, together with his two children and father all lost their lives. The Sheffield workhouse was flooded to a depth of four feet where beds floated about and patients were taken to safety on the next floor.

So much flotsam was piled against Lady's Bridge it diverted the waters down the Wicker and flooded the Midland railway station. A lot of property along the Wicker was ruined by the filthy, mud-laden water that cascaded into cellars and ground floors ruining stock in warehouses and shops, many of which were three feet deep in water. But the flood was slackening and lower down the valley – where Meadow Hall now stands – there were no more deaths, the main damage being the inundation of hundreds of acres of good farmland with mud and debris scattered everywhere which included large quantities of timber, bedsteads, feather beds, tables, grandfather clocks, cupboards, the carcasses of animals (nearly 700 animals were drowned) – and human corpses. Some bodies were taken from the river near Doncaster, twenty-seven miles below the dam.

On the outskirts of Sheffield, Waterloo Houses, a row of terrace houses was completely stripped of the front walls exposing all the interior rooms. Most of the occupants escaped by retreating to their back bedrooms as the flood only just reached the first floor. (from Sheffield Flood by Samuel Harrison)

During the night and the next day bodies were taken to local inns and to the Sheffield workhouse for identification. Many of the thousands of homeless were being clothed and fed and the work of cleaning up the mud and debris began. In the following weeks there were further deaths from typhus and pneumonia. A relief fund was launched and soon raised £50,000 (about £5 million in today's terms). Many workmen gave a day's wages. John Towlerton donated £100. Queen Victoria sent £200 and famous names in the steel industry including Vickers, Rodgers, Mappin, Spear and Jackson, Firth, Brown, Jessop, and Wilkinson each donated either £100 or £200.

The Chief Constable of Sheffield issued the following summary of the damage to property:

	Totally Destroyed	Partly destroyed	Flooded only
Bridges	15	5	
Dwelling houses	39	376	4,086
Factories and forges	12	25	80
Rolling mills and corn mills	4	17	22
Workshops, warehouses, stores	15	13	135
Shops	2	15	451
Public houses and breweries	3	21	162
Churches, chapels and schools	1	–	11
Other buildings	53	14	17
Market gardens	–	287	
Walls and fences	2½ miles		

At the inquest, held on 23rd and 24th March 1864, John Towlerton Leather, John Gunson, Robert (later Sir Robert) Rawlinson, Government Inspector, and Matthew B Jackson, engineer of the Melbourne waterworks, were the principal witnesses. John Webster was the coroner. He explained that the jury were to discover how and by what means Thomas Elston and others had met their deaths. John Towlerton Leather was the first to give evidence. What he said in answer to the coroner's questions was reported fully in The Times. It is his only recorded speech; and it worth hearing how he expressed himself in response to the coroner's questions:

Mr Leather: In 1858 I prepared the plans and specifications for the construction of the Bradfield Reservoir. Parliamentary plans and sections were deposited in 1852 for this and two other reservoirs which we call the Bradfield Scheme. I examined the country generally to see if water could be obtained. Originally, the embankment was set out lower down the valley than it was executed. The first embankment was never commenced because it was found, on trial holes being sunk, that there had been a disturbance of the strata. I then altered my plans for the embankment to where it now is. I examined the ground. The geological formation is just at the outcrop of the coal measures, and the commencement of the millstone grit. The strata consist first of soil, then clay, then stone, then shale, with a gannister formation and a little coal in the centre of the valley. The only spring I ever saw in the valley was one in the site of the reservoir a little above the embankment.

The first thing in forming an embankment is to sink the puddle trench in the centre of the base. The original plan provides for a puddle bank about ten feet below the surface. In sinking a trench we did not find a good foundation at that depth. It was not sufficiently watertight. It was therefore necessary to sink until we did get to a watertight foundation. We sank to a depth varying from ten to sixty feet, and got a watertight foundation. A good deal of water came into the puddle trench during the working. We got rid of it by pumping. I walked over the bottom of the trench when it was finished, and know it was watertight. I did not see the whole of the puddle, but what I did see was well put in and good work…

The embankment is 500 feet wide at the base and 12 feet at the top. The inner slope is 2½ inches to one foot and the outer slope the same. The greatest height is 95 feet. The puddle is four feet wide at the top and sixteen feet wide at the base. There is sixty feet of puddle below the surface, making the total depth of the puddle wall 155 feet. The reservoir would contain a little over 114,000,000 cubic feet of water. The surface area of water was about 78 acres. The area of the gathering ground is about 43,000 acres. We got the material for making the embankment from the inside of the reservoir, and in doing so bared the rocks. In places we got a good deal of stone. The embankment is made of stone, clay, shale and earth. I cannot say how the material was put in. Mr Gunson was not my servant. He was the resident engineer. He had the superintendence of the works, occasionally consulting with me. He could not deviate from my plans.

There are two eighteen inch pipes from the inside to the outside of the reservoir underneath the embankment. The pipes are about 500 feet long, made in lengths of nine feet. They are joined with sockets and lead in the ordinary way. They are laid in a trench nine feet below the surface of the ground. They are wrapped around with clay puddle to the thickness, I think, 18 inches, the trench then being filled in. The valves are at the lower end of the pipe, outside the embankment. If one of the pipes were to burst in the centre, it would be difficult to get to it to repair it. It would have to be reached by excavations. An instance of that kind occurred in the great dam at Crooks. The pipes were originally of wood. I removed them by excavating, and substituted iron pipes. That would be thirty years ago. The breaking of one of those pipes would most likely cause serious damage to the embankment. The pipes were made double the usual strength. I should think there could not be an unequal pressure upon the pipes from the embankment. The Water Company have other dams constructed on the same principle as this, which have been in operation for a great number of years.

Mr Rawlinson: Is it not a common thing for a new line of mains to have blemished joints, and leak?

Mr Leather: The pipes of the company are severely tested before they are put down.

Mr Rawlinson: I saw the testing apparatus, but nevertheless the question is a proper one. My experience is that they do give way.

Mr Leather: My experience is to the contrary; they scarcely ever do give way. I do not know that there was such a case in Birmingham. It would not have been better to have made a culvert for the pipes. Laying them in a trench is better, because in my judgement it is more secure. In case of an accident a culvert would give readier access for repair, but with much greater liability to accident.

When the water flows through freely through the pipes they are not likely to sustain much injury. The opening of the valve would not have a tendency to wrench the joints of the pipes. The pressure lessens as the valve is opened.

The Coroner: One of those valves took half an hour in opening on the night of the inundation, and there was a shaking and a straining of the pipe during the opening, not felt before or after. That is the reason for the question. Would there not be a greater pressure upon the valve when the water was in motion?

Mr Leather: No. There would be a greater disturbance in the way of noise in opening the valve, but the pressure would diminish as the valve opened. The pipes would run off 10,000 cubic feet per minute. Every inch that the water lowered would diminish the pressure of the water upon the embankment. About nine days would be required to let off the whole of the water.

The Coroner: Don't you think it necessary to have some more complete control over the water?

Mr Leather: I have not thought so hitherto. One cannot say how such a thing as this may change one's views. There may be great damage in letting the water off too rapidly in order to relieve the embankment.

The Coroner: Not so much as in letting the whole off at once?

Mr Leather: I did all that I thought necessary to provide against danger.

The Coroner: Ought you not, as a practical engineer, to minimise the danger as much as possible in making these large reservoirs? There has been no attempt to minimise the danger here.

Mr Leather: Oh yes there has…

The Coroner: No there has not; and there is no use in having an engineer unless he does that. You have had the management of these dams. You have placed a great embankment there, and collected an immense body of water behind it. But even though there was a suspicion that the embankment might give way, you have provided no means of taking the water in any other direction, so as to avoid its coming down in one body upon the people of Sheffield. I ask you is it not desirable in such cases that some means should be taken of lessening the danger?

Mr Leather: I cannot conceive of any other way than that adopted…

The Coroner: The embankment was 90 feet high at the centre. If this weight pressed the pipes down at the centre through the puddle, would it not necessarily disjoint the pipes?

Mr Leather: No.

Mr Rawlinson called the attention of the witness to a report published by the Institution of Civil Engineers in which it was stated that pipes laid under an entrenchment occasionally broke from pressure upon them not being equal; and mentioning an instance in Melbourne where the fracture had to be repaired by inserting a line of boiler plating inside.

Mr Leather replied that the pipes in the case cited were lain in the embankment, not in a trough. Those in the Bradfield reservoir were laid in a trench under the embankment. The cases, therefore, were quite different.

The Coroner: But though the trough was made in natural ground, the pipes themselves were laid in an artificial ground, which might offer more resistance in one part than another.

Mr Leather: There were eighteen inches of puddle round them, but they would adjust themselves in the puddle.

The Jury: How do you determine the strength of the embankment?

Mr Leather: It was ten times that of the pressure against it. The pipes have not been examined since the flood. But as there was no leakage through or about the pipes before the accident, and as there was a full flow of water through the pipes when the valves were opened, it is fair to presume there was no leakage. I have seen the valves work under half the pressure.

Mr Perronet Thompson, barrister to the water company continued to examine Mr Leather.

Mr Leather: I have been the consulting engineer of the company in respect of all their reservoirs. I have not previously had an accident, though some of the reservoirs are of greater extent than the Bradfield reservoir. The embankment of the upper dam at Redmires is much larger. The plans and sections for this and for the reservoirs that have stood for years are precisely the same in principle, and there is a great similarity in situation and materials of some of the dams. I used all the means known to me as a practical engineer in the construction of these dams for ensuring the security of the work. So far as my observation went, the quality of the work was good throughout. The fact of the puddle trench being sunk to a depth of sixty feet, is an illustration of the care exercised in providing for the safety of the dam. The specification provided for the trench being made deeper than ten feet if necessary… I have taken all reasonable means to provide against danger. The object of an embankment is to confine the water, and the business of an engineer is to make his embankment sufficient to resist the pressure of the water against it, not to provide any other means of letting the water off on the supposition that the embankment is not strong enough.

Mr Thompson: The puddle wall is the real security of the water. The only object of the embankment is to support the puddle wall, not itself to keep out the water. It is not, therefore, specially important that the earth of the embankment itself should be such as will keep water out.

The Coroner: If an embankment is to support a puddle wall, and the embankment is insufficiently strong, the puddle bank will, of course, fall?

Mr Leather: Yes.

The Coroner: Have you examined the embankment since the flood?

Mr Leather: Yes.

The Coroner: Do you think it is properly made?

Mr Leather: Yes.

The Coroner: Is the higher side made in the same way as the lower?

Mr Leather: Under the lower side there is a footing of stone, to prevent the embankment slipping.

The Coroner: What is the cause of the embankment bursting?

Mr Leather: I really do not know.

The Coroner: What do you conjecture to have been the cause?

Mr Leather: I have very great difficulty indeed in forming any opinion – exceedingly great. I have no opinion worth relying upon. I can form conjectures, and so can anybody else, but they are not worth much.

The Coroner: What is your conjecture?

Mr Leather: There is a possibility of a landslip under the seat of the embankment having produced it, but that I cannot tell. I do not believe the embankment itself has slipped, but the stratification beneath it may have slipped.

Mr Rawlinson: You mean that you do not think the embankment was the first to slip?

Mr Leather: That is the more correct way of putting it.

The Coroner: Have you any more suggestions to offer? A fracture of the pipes has been suggested.

Mr Leather: If the pipes had broken, that might have caused it; but we have no indication of any such breakage.

The Coroner: Why do you hazard the conjecture that there has been a landslip beneath the embankment?

Mr Leather: Because we know they do take place; a landslip has taken place in this valley below the dam, and in many other valleys. It would be a slip of the surface not the rock.

The Coroner: You do not ascribe the bursting of the reservoir to unsound principles of engineering or to bad workmanship?

Mr Leather: Certainly not.

Mr Rawlinson: Was the embankment formed by waggons and tips, by barrows, or by both?

Mr Leather: You had better ask Mr Gunson on that point.

The Coroner: Suppose the percolating water was not stopped by the puddle, but went through the rocks at a lower level than the bottom of the puddle trench, might it not have the effect of washing down the embankment on the low side of the puddle bank?

Mr Leather: No. The probability is that it would find its way to a spring lower down the valley.

The Coroner: Have you seen the embankment of the Rivington waterworks, Lancashire?

Mr Leather: No.

The Coroner: Are you aware the reservoir bottom there was quarried the same as yours?; and that subsequently a large quantity of water found its way below the stratification of the puddle bank and leaked out at a considerable distance from the embankment?

Mr Leather: That is probably so, but I do not know of it.

The coroner then closely questioned John Gunson who showed details of the plans, and explained the laying of the pipes, the puddle trench and so on, leading up to the day in question when John Gunson visited the dam.

Rawlinson, the Government Inspector, did not want feelings to run high and thought that nothing would be gained by either incriminating the engineers or by calling further witnesses. He was so selective in witnesses that only one of them – John Gunson – had actually been present during the construction of the dam and he was the only one who had witnessed the bursting of the dam. Robert Rawlinson concluded that the embankment had been badly constructed, that material had been tipped in layers that were too thick, that building material should not have been taken from within the reservoir and that the burying of pipelines was bad practice. John Towlerton showed how much care he had taken over the specification of the clay corewall and how he attached the greatest importance in having a deep and watertight foundation for it. He said the collapse was caused by a landslide.

The inquest found that the deaths were due to drowning as a result of the bursting of the reservoir, and the jury added: 'There has not been that engineering skill and the attention to the construction of the works, which their magnitude and importance demanded'.

In later years there would have been a full public enquiry, but this one was brought to an abrupt close after only two days. It was a period of history when the people of the Loxley valley – including the dead, the homeless and the subsequent jobless – had no vote and no voice. They were working class.

The Sheffield Waterworks Company engaged five of the finest water engineers of the day to report on the dam. They were Thomas Hawksley (Nottingham and Liverpool waterworks), J F Bateman (Manchester and Glasgow waterworks), James Simpson (Chelsea, Lambeth, Newcastle and Bristol waterworks), T E Harrison and John (later Sir John) Fowler. In the report they all agreed that the dam collapsed as a result of a landslide and that the accident was unavoidable.

Sheffield Corporation who wanted to purchase the water company asked a further nine eminent engineers to give individual reports. They included Sir Charles

Rennie, Henry Coneybeare (Bombay waterworks), James Leslie (Edinburgh and Dundee waterworks) and Matthew Jackson (Melbourne waterworks). Generally, they agreed with Robert Rawlinson's conclusions that the embankment had been poorly constructed.

Any study of the failure of the dam has to take into account the crack near the top of the embankment, the fact that men were walking over the embankment an hour before it collapsed – presumably over what they considered solid ground – and the remarkable speed of collapse. In the late 1970s, Geoffrey M Binnie FRS, experienced water engineer, made a study of the failure of the dam in a paper to the Geological Society of London[35]. His conclusions were still debatable. Soon after that he made an amazing discovery. He found on microfilm an old drawing of the long section of the dam and puddle trench. It was simply labelled: 'Sheffield Waterworks, Contract No 4'. He immediately knew it referred to Dale Dyke and finally knew the reason for the collapse! The drawing showed how the base of the puddle trench had deep steps in it, one step dropping thirty-five feet and another, ten feet[36].

In 1877 Sir Alexander R Rennie (Geoffrey Binnie's grandfather) wrote:

> Formerly it was the custom to finish off the bottom of the trench longitudinally into long level benches divided by abrupt vertical steps; but this is very dangerous practice, for it must be remembered that clay puddle is a very plastic and compressible substance, and apt to crack under unequal strain…

John Towlerton Leather had not accounted for the effect of different amounts of settling from one place to another (known as differential consolidation) due to the sudden changes in thickness of clay at the steps in the trench. He had tried too hard. He had gone to great pains to have the trench dug down to sixty feet below the floor

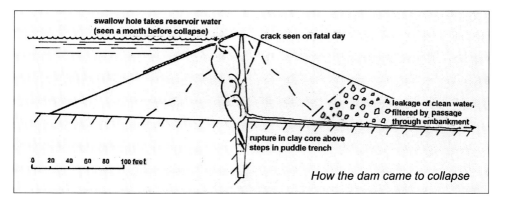

How the dam came to collapse

[35] Geoffrey M Binnie, *The Collapse of the Dale Dyke Dam in Retrospect* (Quarterly Journal of Engineering Geology, 1978)

[36] Geoffrey M Binnie, *Early Victorian Water Engineers* (Thomas Telford, 1981).

of the valley so that the dam would be watertight, but in making big vertical steps along the bottom of the trench, he was digging the dam's grave. Over a period of a few months, compaction of the puddle clay produced shearing or cracking in the clay immediately above each step, providing a space for water to enter. In normal circumstances the presence of water helps to keep the clay watertight. But a rupture provided space for water to move around. But where was this water coming from and where was it going?

The breach, photographed the morning after. (Sheffield Libraries)

There had been problems of too much water seeping into the puddle trench during excavation and two steam engines were kept working for a period of two years to keep it free of water. The puddling was the careful layering of kneaded clay in the trench, six inches at a time and, once the clay core was finished, settling would begin. The settling squeezed out some of the water in the puddle clay so it would be natural to see muddy water escaping from the works. Later on, with continued settling of the clay, rupturing would have occurred above each step in the trench. Water in the pores of the material of the embankment began to seep into the cracks and to erode the core clay, slowly producing a hollow and draining out through the permeable downstream shoulder. The cavity had plenty of time to grow bigger and migrate higher. There must have been plenty of water issuing from the toe of the dam, though that may not have appeared to be anything unusual.

After the inquest an employee gave a statement to the engineer Matthew Jackson. A month before the collapse a hollow had appeared in the pitching on the reservoir side, with water apparently seeping into the embankment in a whirlpool. By the day of the collapse there must have been a considerable amount of water passing from the reservoir through a large cavity or pothole in the centre of the dam. Slight slumping then caused the crack, seen on the downstream bank on the fatal day, and the sudden sinking of the top of the dam into the cavity explains the speed of collapse. The same employee wrote of his experience minutes before the collapse:

> …it was observed that the water was lowering faster than the pipes could draw it off. The contractors then sent a man along the bank with a light to see whether the water was escaping. He came running back to say there was a hole blown through. Mr Gunson, George Swindon and others immediately went over the top of the embankment. I went as far as I thought safe, and saw the water boiling through. I stood about ten minutes and then the top fell in, which appeared to stop the water a minute or two, until the water ran over the top in sheets of foam. An immense gap speedily opened…

The mystery of the reason for the collapse of the Dale Dyke Dam has been solved though it took over a century to discover. In the years after the accident changes came about in dam building: pipes were not put beneath the embankment, finer material was put nearest to the core with coarser to the outside, a drain at the toe caught leaking water and, later on, steps in the puddle trench were substituted by gradual slopes. But not until sixty years later were there regular inspections during construction.

Soon things in the Loxley valley began to return to normal. Many Factories, houses and bridges were rebuilt and men returned to work, though a small number of ruins remained. Today there are few reminders of the catastrophe. There are still one or two buildings that have a line on them to show where the flood came up to and a few sad headstones at High Bradfield, Loxley and in Sheffield cemeteries. No lasting memorial was ever built though there had been suggestions, for example by Samuel Harrison the editor of *The Sheffield Times* and author of the first book on the disaster. In 1964 a hundred years afterwards there was a revival of memories when local newspapers featured the story of the disaster, and among older people you may still hear the phrase '…it only happens once every Sheffield Flood'.

John Towlerton Leather's career miraculously survived. He continued with his projects at Portland and Portsmouth, though he was never knighted like other engineers of his time. He must have been bewildered by the failure of the dam after all the care he had given it. The human disaster shook him considerably, and troubled him for the rest of his life. On his 79th birthday he reflected with much self doubt: 'I can now see many things that I ought not to have done and many others that I ought to have done—and these sins weigh heavily upon me at times when reflection forces them on my memory.' He was no showman, and took the loss of life very much to heart. He is listed as giving £100 in aid of the victims, but family tradition has it that, out of his own pocket, he pensioned dependants who had lost relatives and nearly bankrupted himself in doing so.

Three years earlier in 1861, J T Leather had already been offered the biggest and most challenging contract of his career – that of the Spithead Forts, a vital part of the defence of the realm. His contract went ahead as planned and was to keep him occupied for another eleven years. By coincidence, just six days after the collapse of Dale Dyke dam, J T Leather purchased a site in Hunslet south of Leeds with a view to setting his son up in the business of building steam locomotives, and the Hunslet Engine Company. Then in 1867, Contractor Leather was asked by the Admiralty to be contractor for the extension of Portsmouth Dockyard, a £2¼ million scheme.

Portrait of JTL (drawing by C W Walton)

Steam Engines, Sea Forts, and Docks

The Hunslet Engine Company   The tramway from the Brandling's Middleton Colliery to the coal wharves on the south bank of the River Aire in Leeds was the world's first commercial steam railway and its first locomotive – built to Trevithick's design – was tried out there on 24 June 1812. As a boy John Towlerton Leather had seen the steam engine pulling the coal trucks backwards and forwards along the line that ran within half a mile of his family home at Beeston Park, and witnessed the early history of locomotive building, in which he was to play a part. Matthew Murray built four steam engines at the Round Foundry in Holbeck specifically for the Middleton tramway, which actually went on working until 1835. At that time Murray built locomotive steam engines only when asked, his normal run of business being stationary engines and machine tools. However, by the end of the 1820s, the railway era had begun and in the next decade or so to 1843 the firm, which by then had become 'Fenton Murray and Jackson', had made many more locomotives. A total of fifty-three were built and they included as many as twenty '7-foot gauge' express engines for the Great Western Railway. The firm of Fenton, Murray and Jackson closed down in 1843, after which the works were known as the Victoria Foundry.

Nearby in Hunslet, Charles Todd, who had learnt his trade with Matthew Murray, established the Airedale Foundry with James Kitson. But soon Charles Todd left to start up the new 'Railway Foundry' with partner John Shepherd. From 1840 this small concern was on the site of the future Hunslet Engine Company and twenty locomotives were built up to 1845. Charles Todd moved on again in 1844 to set up on his own on Dewsbury Road, leaving Shepherd to find a new partner for the Railway Foundry in Edward Brown Wilson. In his history of the Hunslet Engine Company, *The Hunslet Hundred*, L T C Rolt remarks, that in E B Wilson David Shepherd had found 'a remarkably enterprising, vigorous and ambitious man, so much so that the name of Shepherd slips out of the records'. The Railway Foundry attracted some fine engineers and expanded rapidly under E B Wilson. The *Jenny Lind* was their most famous and successful engine. It was designed by the young David Joy and introduced the high-pressure boiler.

In 1852 a 0-4-0 tank engine, with four foot driving wheels named 'Queen', was purchased from the Railway Foundry by John Towlerton Leather's Portland

Breakwater Construction Company. Two years later a second tank engine from the Railway Foundry went to work on the Portland Breakwater. About 1854 a standard 0-6-0 tank engine with three-foot driving wheels was bought by JTL for his colliery at Waterloo Main at Temple Newsam. This particular engine also served in the Crimean war. At the siege of Sebastopol, thirty thousand soldiers lived through the severe winter of 1854-55 and were suffering from cholera, inadequate food and cold. An improved supply line to the coast was imperative. A short railway was built from Balaclava, twenty-nine miles inland from where the troops were stationed, by contractor Thomas Brassey. Released from Waterloo Main Colliery, the steam engine was renamed *The Alliance* and dispatched from the Railway Foundry early in September 1855. The Railway Foundry was a flourishing concern, and a second engine was ordered for the Crimea a few days later; but in 1856 E B Wilson died still in his prime, and, two years later the firm closed down.

The Railway Foundry had been built up into one of the largest and most successful locomotive building firms in the country. The manager of the stationary engine workshop and chief cashier of the firm was none other than Charles Wetherell Wardle, husband of John Towlerton Leather's sister Liz. As the firm was closing, Alexander Campbell arrived on the scene, from Greenock, to set up a new partnership with Charles Wardle and John Manning, who provided the capital. Having acquired land alongside the former Railway Foundry, the new company of Manning Wardle and Company was founded as the Boyne Engine Works, named after the Viscount Boyne who had owned the land. The firm was able to take not only skilled workmen from the old Railway Foundry but also designs of locomotives and parts of locomotives. The Boyne Engine Works continued in business until 1927.

On 31 October 1860 one of the first locomotives from the Boyne Engine Works was delivered to John Towlerton Leather's Waterloo Main Colliery at Temple Newsam, Leeds. Locomotive number 16 was a 9½ inch cylinder tank engine which was tried in steam and dispatched the same day. Three further tank engines from the Boyne works were purchased for Waterloo Main, one on 20 June 1862, another on 7 September 1863 and the last, ten years later, on 3 November 1873. Each Locomotive was named *Waterloo Main Colliery*, and numbered. Number Two was later sent to Portsmouth for work on the dockyard and renamed *Lady Portsmouth*.

The Railway Foundry with extensive land and workshops were auctioned off in lots in 1860 at the Scarborough Hotel in Leeds. Some of it went to Hudswell Clarke and Company, while Kitson and Company purchased another lot. Both were locomotive-building concerns. There were now three locomotive firms in Hunslet – and still room for a fourth. On 17 March 1864 J T Leather bought the remaining site for £2,766 and founded the Hunslet Engine Company.

In setting up the new company, JTL had his sights on a possible career for his second son Arthur Hugo Leather. Arthur Hugo had been educated at Rugby School, followed by Trinity College Cambridge and was eighteen at the time. JTL also required a good and reliable manager to run the business. He consulted Alexander Campbell of Manning Wardle who recommended his own son. Twenty-six year old James Campbell had returned from engineering work with the East India Railway and had acquired a good deal of experience in the industry. James Campbell took over as manager of the new Hunslet Engine Company, and so began a long association between the Campbell family and the firm. James Campbell was soon joined in Hunslet by his brother George. A close family link was established between Manning Wardle and the Hunslet Engine Company. Both firms concentrated on industrial locomotives, but the steady demand kept them both occupied. Parts made by one firm were purchased by the other, and vice versa.

We can only imagine the details of the processes of locomotive building. The day started at 6.00am and continued until 6.00 in the evening. The workshops would be rather dark places, poorly lit with oil lamps and tallow candles with a glow from the forge or rivet hearth. In the boiler shop all the rivets were put in by hand while the boiler smith, using Yorkshire iron, shaped plate flanges with the help of strikers who hammered the metal over blocks. The strikers were among the least well paid.

In the smiths' shop at the back there was a steam hammer to deal with the heaviest forgings, but much of the work would be done by hand. In the copper shop the smiths fashioned copper fire boxes and brass tubes. The machine shop had steam power for turning metal on the lathes but no overhead gantry or travelling cranes. For lifting they relied on a simple jib crane mounted on a turntable, otherwise jacks were used, for example when putting the wheels on the locomotive. The early Hunslet works had no foundry and castings came from other firms nearby such as Manning Wardle. Pattern makers working in wood made 'models', which were then sent to be cast. These included such things as wheel centres.

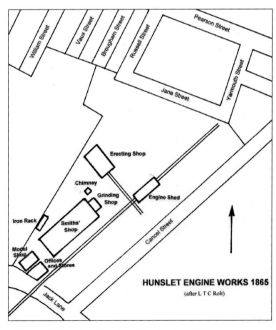

HUNSLET ENGINE WORKS 1865
(after L T C Rolt)

In July 1868, it is recorded that J T Leather's son Arthur Hugo (he was 22 at the time)

Plan of Hunslet Engine Works in 1865. (after L T C Rolt)

- 111 -

was sent as a fitter to carry out running repairs to a locomotive in Portsmouth. The return ticket from Leeds to Portsmouth cost £1-0s-7d and Arthur was given a special allowance of 1/6d! South Leeds was becoming the biggest centre for the building of steam locomotives in the world – except perhaps for Berlin. It took a few months for the new Hunslet Engine Works to build up enough parts to be able to assemble and start selling its locomotives. The order book is now with Leeds Industrial Museum at Armley Mills and shows the first locomotive, named Linden, was a saddle tank sold in July 1865 to Brassey and Ballard, the railway contractors for the Midland Railway extension to St Pancras. The very same steam engine was rediscovered 100 years later in a Yorkshire colliery, but too late – the old saddle tank, converted to a tank engine and unrecognised, was broken for scrap only weeks before it was tracked down as the very first locomotive to leave the Hunslet works. The second

The first locomotive in The Hunslet Engine Company's Order Book is named Linden. It was a saddle tank sold in July 1865 to Brassey and Ballard, the railway contractors for the Midland Railway extension to St Pancras. (L.H. Group Services Ltd)

one went in October 1865 to JTL's colliery at Waterloo Main. Another released on the same day went initially to W and J Pickering of Barnstaple, Devon, but was later purchased by Leather, Smith and Company and renamed 'Portsmouth'. Three similar engines went to the well-known Waring Brothers at Kensington, St Pancras and Barnet, all in London. The tenth engine, another saddle tank, was destined for Java, via Rotterdam. Others went as far afield as Prince Edward Island, Canada, and the Rio Tinto mines in southern Spain; six tank engines went to the East Indies. In the four years between December 1867 and September 1871 as many as fifteen saddle tank engines went to Leather, Smith and Co for use in the Portsmouth Dockyard extensions. Many of the early locos were of matching design (see illustration), with a 0-6-0 specification, that is, they had six large, linked driving wheels, 3ft 4ins in diameter, and no small (or bogey) wheels. They were built as work horses for use in coal mines, railway construction, dock works and similar situations, and were ideal for pulling and pushing a few wagons over short distances all day long year in year out. In 1870 the first of twenty narrow (1 foot 10⅓ inch) gauge locomotives was supplied to the Dinorwic quarries in North Wales.

In 1870 the first of twenty narrow gauge (1 foot 10⅓ inch) locomotives was supplied to the Dinorwic quarries in North Wales. (L.H. Group Services Ltd)

The wages book from the Hunslet Engine Works shows the number of employees, which within a year or so grew to about a hundred. They included fitters, boiler makers, smiths, pattern makers, turners, machine men, strikers, apprentices and labourers. For a sixty-hour week they earned between twenty and thirty shillings, according to the skill of the job. Arthur Leather was working as an apprentice until 1869 when his name appears for the first time in the wage book. He continued there until late in 1871, but it seems that he was not very interested in a future with the locomotive building industry and went on to become a manufacturer in the woollen industry of Bradford.

On 16 September 1871 James Campbell, in a letter to John Towlerton Leather, asked if he would consider selling the business on easy terms. JTL took a few weeks to think over the proposition and replied on 26 October:

> I have spoken to Mr Arthur on the subject of disposing of the Hunslet Engine Works and he offers no objection provided I sustain no loss in the endeavour I have made to give him a start in life. The question of price therefore depends upon what view I may take of it, but I may say at once that I would accept less from you, and grant easier terms, than I would to anyone else. By saying this I believe I am affording you an opportunity of a lifelong settlement of a more favourable kind than is ever likely to occur again...'

James Campbell made calculations as to the value of the firm and the profits owed, and contacted his father Alexander Campbell (of the Boyne Engine Works) who promised financial help. Five days later James Campbell made an offer for purchase of the Hunslet Engine Company of £24,500. Allowing for the interest on deferred payments, the final sum agreed was £25,000 payable in five instalments at six monthly intervals between 1 January 1872 and 1 December 1873. As soon as the first payment was made James Campbell took possession of the firm.

The sum of £25,000 was a high figure but took into account the developments that had recently taken place in the works. These included the addition of a new pattern shop, copper shop and more offices. In 1865 only four locomotives were built but after that an average of nine were sold each year until 1871, when seventeen locomotives were supplied. Output had nearly doubled in the few months leading up to the sale. No doubt JTL was very satisfied at the outcome, appreciating that he had been able to equip his colliery at Waterloo Main and supply his work on Portsmouth Dockyard with many fine locomotives at cost price.

The Hunslet Engine Company continued to send locomotives all over the world, including Russia, India, Kenya, Nigeria, the Gold Coast, Cape Town, Western Australia, Peru, Java, France and Spain; locos operated from the depth of British coalmines to the top of Snowdon, from Welsh slate quarries to the London Underground and, of course, in many other localities. The word 'Hunslet' became well known to railway enthusiasts who still see many of the old steam engines on preserved railway lines and in museums. The firm was still doing well in the 1980s, so much so that in 1982 the Managing Director was able to say that Hunslet Holdings was the seventeenth most profitable British manufacturer in terms of return on equity. But soon things went wrong. By the early 1990s after two failing takeovers and political decisions following the privatisation of British Rail, the

Hunslet Engine Works came to a sad demise. This was in spite of the production of specialist equipment for the Channel Tunnel and other diesel-hydraulics for use in Borneo as well as passenger diesel units. By November 1995 the last remnants of the firm at Jack Lane Hunslet were sold off and with them, the end of the era of locomotive building in Leeds.

The Spithead Forts In the decade or two leading to 1860, relations between Britain and France were still strained, and many feared that France might take revenge for Trafalgar and Waterloo. The French naval dockyard at Cherbourg looked threatening, and by 1860 steam-driven, ironclad warships had been developed, as well as a much more powerful long-range cannon – the

Spitbank Fort seen from the air in 2005. (Vail Williams)

Armstrong gun. The government reviewed the defences along Britain's south coast, and a Royal Commission was set up which reported in February 1860. The Commission advised the construction of fortifications to protect naval bases at Plymouth, Portland, Portsmouth, Pembroke and the Thames estuary. Portsmouth and its approaches were deemed particularly crucial. The Commission stressed the strategic importance of the security of the naval anchorage at Spithead and the protection of the dockyard at Portsmouth. Spithead is part of the Solent, a four-mile wide channel between the Isle of Wight and the mainland. It was along this channel that the defence plan proposed the construction of a series of five forts to defend the approach to Portsmouth harbour. They were to be known as the Spithead Forts. Tenders were put out early in 1861 for 'Works and Repairs to the Fortifications, Barracks and other buildings at Portsmouth, and Detached Works not exceeding five miles'.

A long debate ensued as to whether the forts were really necessary. Gladstone wanted a more peaceful way forward, with freer trade and cuts in taxes; while Lord Palmerston thought the United Kingdom should be adequately defended against foreign invasion, and the expenditure budgeted for. There was much argument as to whether forts were a better defence than armed ships. During this dispute Gladstone threatened to resign on more than one occasion. Palmerston's reply was that it was better to lose Mr Gladstone than to lose Portsmouth. In the end Gladstone kept his post and Palmerston his forts. Construction was delayed and the final decision to build was passed in Parliament in 1863.

Civil engineer John Hawkshaw FRS (later Sir John and president of the Institution of Civil Engineers[37]) was appointed chief engineer for the fortifications and the planning of five forts. Having been engaged on the Halifax-Bradford railway and the Leeds-Thirsk railway – including the dual level station complex in Leeds – John Hawkshaw would have been well acquainted with the Leather engineers. In 1861 the main contract for the forts was offered to John Towlerton Leather. JTL had built up an excellent reputation with his work on the Portland Breakwater and being asked to undertake the new construction was further to his credit. The offer included all the arrangements for carrying out the works: the making of concrete-blocks, the provision of steam engines, steam cranes and pile drivers, the erection of a shipping pier, special barges for transport, and circular stages for the construction work. He was engaged under the general supervision of the Royal Engineers Department. The resident manager was his old friend and colleague Edward Pease Smith, and his agent Mr W Hill.

The original plan was that five Spithead forts would be situated at No Man's Land, at Horse Sand, one between Horse Sand and Portsea Island, one on Spit Sand; and the fifth at Sturbridge. This was considered the best layout for the defences of the Spithead channel. During the three years delay, engineers carried out extensive examination of the seabed. There was no problem with No Man's Land and Horse Sand, but at Spit Sand and Sturbridge the seabed was of mud and quicksand, and in no state to support the foundations of large forts. Sturbridge and the one between Horse Sand and Portsea Island were withdrawn

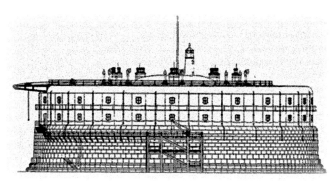

No Man's Land Fort, over 200 feet across. This and Horse Sand Fort are half as big again as Spitbank. (after G H Mitchell)

---

[37] Sir John Hawkshaw (1811-1891) was born in Leeds. He was engineer for Portsmouth Dockyard Extension and Spithead Forts, Maryport Docks, Wellington Street Railway Complex, Leeds, and Lockwood Viaduct, Huddersfield. He was consulting engineer for Charing Cross and Canon Street Stations and the Inner Circle underground railway in London; and also chief engineer for the Severn Tunnel and the Amsterdam Ship Canal

completely and two smaller forts were proposed to replace Spit Sand: one on Spitbank and one on Ryde Sand. Finally Ryde Sand, after building had started, was considered too difficult to make secure foundations, and a smaller fort was substituted off St Helen's Point. In the end only four island sea forts were built, the two large ones of No Man's Land and Horse Sand, and two smaller ones of Spitbank and St Helen's. Each fort was built on a sandbank where the seabed was shallow – almost uncovered at low tide. They were man-made islands and everything had to be brought to the site by boat.

The forts are circular with a hollow centre. The two larger ones measure 210 feet in diameter on a base 230 feet across, while the smaller ones are 150 feet in diameter. In the spring of 1864 Contractor Leather began work on the foundations. Those of Horse Sand fort go down to a depth of eleven feet below the seabed, while those of No Man's Land needed an additional ten feet in order to establish a firm foundation. The circular stone rampart of the base – fifty feet thick – is built up with Cornish granite on the outside and Bramley Fall and Portland stone on the inside. The intervening space – the wall cavity – is filled with massive concrete blocks, made in moulds on the mainland. Bramley Fall stone came from near Leeds and the original quarry supplied very large blocks of coarse-grained pebbly sandstone (the Rough Rock of the Millstone Grit Group). It was well suited for engineering work, and known for its strength and resistant qualities. The old Bramley Fall Quarry closed in 1829 but the name persisted and subsequent supplies came from the nearby working quarries on the banks of the River Aire, west of Leeds.

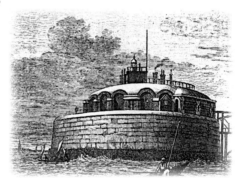

The central part of the base ring was filled with clay and gravel before a thick layer of concrete was laid down to support the superstructure. The whole of the flat base reached to a foot or so above the level of the highest spring tide. On this base a fifteen-foot thick wall, sixteen feet high, was constructed. On the outside were placed large granite blocks from Cornwall, each one very slightly bowed to follow the curve of the fort wall with, on the inside, blocks of Portland roachstone.

Spitbank Fort in 1872 from the south side. (The Graphic)

Each granite block weighed about eight tons. The plan for the large forts included 149 guns in two tiers, the whole to be finished with five turrets on the roof and a lighthouse in the centre. The forts had three levels with eight-foot thick floors and roof, and each level was divided into smaller chambers and divisions in a circular plan. The basement housed forty shell and cartridge stores in two rings while in the centre there was a coal store, laundry and kitchen. The next level was the lower gun floor with space for guns round the perimeter, while centrally were the officers' quarters. The upper gun floor was similar but with more space given to the larger number of soldiers quarters, and there was a central courtyard, open to the sky. An artesian well brought up fresh water.

The smaller fort of Spitbank had a basement built on the same lines as the two larger forts but with a diameter of 150 feet. The superstructure was planned to be clad with iron on the seaward side only, mounting fifteen guns. The date 1870 is carved above the entrance and there is a complex interior architecture on two levels with cramped accommodation for 156 men in three tiers of hammocks, though these were never filled to capacity. Each small room has a beautiful, vaulted, brickwork ceiling. Heating was from coal-fired stoves and lighting by oil lamps and candles.

St Helen's fort was sited off St Helen's Point, Isle of Wight, where the sand is just about uncovered at spring tides. Initially, it was planned to build on the point itself, but this scheme was abandoned for an island fort. The foundations were started in 1867 using a different method, sinking a ring of iron caissons twenty-five feet into the seabed. They passed through sand and shingle and finally five feet of hard clay. The caissons kept back the sea, sand was dredged out and the space filled with a ten-foot thick bed of concrete, bringing the base of the fort to two feet above low water at spring tides. By 1869 the outer wall was completed. However, a settling of the foundations produced a slight tilt of the basement, which led to a revised design of a simpler and asymmetrical superstructure. It was to have six heavy guns facing the sea and four lighter ones on the landward side.

Much of the design for the construction works for the forts was carried out by J T Leather's associate and Resident Manager, Edward Pease Smith, who made use of the system he designed for the fort at the end of the Portland Breakwater, that of tipping deposits from a large circular staging. After the foundations were completed, he built up the masonry by using 'radiating steam-girder travellers of wide span, upon which the steam crabs could command any point below them'. This ingenious system was used to particular effect on both the Spithead and Gilkicker forts. E P Smith also designed a system for making concrete blocks using wooden moulds, a shipping pier on the mainland, special barges for transporting the heavy blocks of stone and concrete; and the special plant required. The centre of operations was the contractors' yard at Stokes Bay where stone was dressed and laid out as it would be on the site and where the concrete blocks were moulded. It is noted that during the whole of the construction of the forts there was 'not a single accident of a serious character happened throughout, and the arrangements were in fact almost perfect'[38].

In July 1865, Lord Napier examined 'the foundations and basement walls on the great marine forts on the No-man, Horse, St Helen's and Spit Shoals, and also on the western approaches to Spithead'. They were heralded as 'a wonderful piece of mechanical and engineering skill which would give the world a visible sign of the magnitude of the undertaking which the War Department had on hand', and were 'proof that something unprecedented in size and strength is being realised not only for the protection of Portsmouth, its harbour and dockyard, from bombardment, but also the defence of the extensive anchorage of Spithead, from the mouth of Portland harbour to the Isles of Wight'.

J T Leather was asked to complete the fort at Gilkicker on the mainland following the failure after five months work on the foundations of the first contractor late in 1863 - another example of the trouble-shooting contractor coming in to save the day. Gilkicker was one of a line of seven old forts at Gosport, where a new and solid replacement was required. It was sited on the shore facing Stokes Bay where it could defend the harbour entrance against attack from the sea. The new contract was made, and work recommenced in June 1865. The 400-foot long, semi-circular front of the fort is faced in Cornish granite with twenty-two arches for the twenty-two guns, placed behind iron shields. The fort was fitted out with barrack accommodation for five officers, four sergeants and ninety-eight men. By 1869, the work was nearly finished and described in the report to Parliament as 'skilfully built, both for permanency and for resisting power. There have been no failures of any sort'.

The system of building the stone-work at Gilkicker was that used in the Spithead fort. Both were to Edward Pease Smith's design. A steam crane, operated from an

Three of the forts: north side of Spitbank Fort with Horse Sand on the left and No Man's Land to the right. (The Graphic 17 Feb 1872)

[38] Obituary of John Towlerton Leather in *Proceedings of the Institution of Civil Engineers* vol. 83 p433-436.

overhead gantry, lowered very large blocks of stone into place, and then moved on radially to follow the curve of the walls. Since 1890, the granite outer wall has been covered by an earth embankment.

It was found that some of the passages were a little narrow to allow two men to pass carrying shells from the stores, whereas, in the bigger forts, for safety reasons, there were separate passages, one for carrying the lamps for lighting, and the other for taking live ammunition from the magazines and shell stores. Here, an opening was made for passing the lamps directly into the light boxes avoiding the danger of carrying them through the shell passages.

In July 1868 Lord Napier again inspected the construction work of the sea forts. An enquiry ensued into 'the construction, condition and cost of the fortifications erected or in the course of erection.'[39] The report that followed commended the design and construction of the forts but remarked that the total cost had greatly exceeded the first estimate. This had come about because some of the forts had been enlarged, and iron plating added for greater strength against the new type of guns. It was the iron-work, not in the original plan that took most of the extra expense. The cost of materials and labour had also increased, and there were difficulties in securing foundations in some places. Allegations that the works were insecure had been greatly exaggerated, but 'certain weaknesses had been observed and corrected'. These corrections no doubt included the revised plan for St Helen's fort.

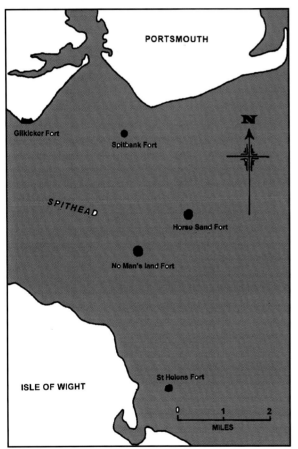

Map of Spithead showing position of sea forts.

[39] Parliamentary Paper No 4135, 'Report of the Committee appointed to enquire into the Construction, Condition, and Costs of the Fortifications erected, or in course of erection' (1869)

Nicknamed 'Palmerston's Folly' during their construction, the forts were the source of ridicule and criticism: 'built on quicksand'; 'cost half the national income'; 'outdated as soon as they were built' and so on. The assertion was made, and quite rightly so, that the sites for the forts had been chosen purely for defensive reasons – according to their proximity to the main shipping channel – with no account of the condition of the seabed in those places. Even the final sites had presented many problems, and all were exposed to storms and heavy seas. The final assessment for each fort, including the ironwork, was £425,000 for Horse Sand, £460,000 for No Man's Land, £180,000 for Spitbank, £125,000 for St Helen's and £110,000 for the Gilkicker fort.

The contract was finished in 1872 and in December J T Leather received a letter from Major Hewitt of the Royal Engineers who said: 'I feel that the completion of so large a contract as that for the Spithead Forts, involving a payment of some £530,000 and extending over 11 years... calls for some acknowledgement of the able, literal and thorough manner in which all arrangements have been made, and the service carried out...' Mr W Hill's accompanying letter is of a more practical nature: 'The construction, simultaneously, of works at several isolated marine sites has been subjected to so many natural impediments and difficulties by reason of weather and other causes and has therefore been a source of constant anxiety that it would have been unbearable not to have got along smoothly in other respects'.

In his reply Contractor Leather touches on the tremendous satisfaction he gained from 'contriving the means by which these Spithead Forts could best be accomplished':

Middleton Hall,
Belford,
Northumberland.
21st Dec 1872.

Sir,

Mr Hill has forwarded your very kind letter on the completion of the Spithead Forts Works of the 13th inst.

It is exceedingly gratifying to me to learn by this means that my efforts to carry out these extensive and difficult works in a thoroughly good and substantial manner have been so far successful as to elicit your approval in terms so entirely satisfactory.

Twenty years ago, little or nothing was known of marine construction of this kind and a reference to the original Contract Drawings and Specification for the foundations of these Forts will shew how little information could then be afforded for the guidance of anyone undertaking to carry out the work.

In working back over the experience in the construction of hydraulic and marine works extending over a period of some 30 or 40 years I cannot call to mind any that have afforded me more real pleasure than that of contriving the means by which these Spithead Forts could best be accomplished and their complete substantiability secured so as to attain the object intended in the best possible manner.

No doubt circumstances have recurred during their execution well calculated to engender questions of difficulty in the settlement of accounts and I may mention by way of example the somewhat capricious stoppage of the works for a considerable time at a very critical period of construction.

On resuming the works, however, that question was fairly met by the Department, as I hope it was by me also, and was equitably settled without reference to any third party; other instances such as the abandonment of the Sturbridge Fort and many minor ones have been encountered but all satisfactorily settled as they arose.

The complete immunity then, from all difficulties or questions which has prevailed throughout the whole period of eleven years during which these works have extended may be attributed perhaps as much to forbearance on the part of the offices in charge and consideration of the difficulties I had to encounter in the simultaneous construction of so many isolated marine works, as to any merit of mine, or of my agents, and I therefore feel that I am all the more indebted to you for the good feeling which actuated now in writing this letter I now most gratefully acknowledge.

I have the honour to be
Sir
Your obedient Servant
J. Towlerton Leather.

To Major Hewett, RE

In fact, the forts never saw any military action, and they stand there today as solid as ever – a reminder of a more turbulent past. They were manned as signal stations during World War I, neglected between the wars, and manned again to witness the air raids in World War II. After that they were no longer of any naval or military interest, and for many years were for sale with no buyers, and ran into disrepair. In 1982 Spitbank was purchased by Shaun Maguire, who restored much of it himself with the help of family and friends. He ran it as a tourist attraction with a large restaurant, discotheque, bar, and roof-top apartment; fresh water being obtainable from the 400 foot deep artesian well. In 1999 Spitbank was offered for sale at £385,000 and Waterside Properties included some interesting information in their brochure:

> The fort is built like a giant doughnut lying flat on the Solent with fresh water well in the middle. Garrison quarters run round the inner wall with the fighting rooms running round the outer wall. The entire fort including the gun rooms, magazines and light tunnel are open for inspection. Wall cards, photographs, life size replicas of the guns and models provide a fascinating insight of life during the time this fort was in active service. There is much original equipment including the flooring and shelves, the voice pipes, lamp globes and small cast iron cooking range which was designed to cater for the entire garrison. One of the rooms is over 400 feet long and runs round the core of the fort and can be explored by the more adventurous with the aid of candle or torch. Access is provided by an external landing stage with an electric overhead hoist to deck level.

No Man's Land fort was also bought and converted to a palatial, luxury home. It has an opulent dining room, several entertaining rooms, a tennis court, swimming pool and its own helicopter pad. It was up for sale in 2000 for £10 million. St Helen's Fort is privately owned too, while Portsmouth Naval Base Historical Trust now owns the unimproved Horse Sand fort. Abandoned for so long, like uninhabited islands, the forts abound with stories of secret passages, of ghosts and mysterious goings on, but they are built to last, and will continue to attract attention for many years to come. All four are now Scheduled Ancient Monuments. They are no longer needed for the defence of the realm, but remain a solid testimonial to Sir John Hawkshaw, Contractor Leather, Edward Pease Smith and all the civil engineers involved.

Portsmouth Dockyard Extensions   With the gigantic civil engineering works of the Portland Breakwater nearing completion and the walls of the sea forts at Portsmouth literally growing up out of the sea, the reputation of Contractor Leather for getting the job done and for overcoming the ferocious forces of storm and tide was known far beyond the south coast of England. Not only across Europe: the accomplishments of Contractor Leather also filtered into the higher echelons of the War Office and the Admiralty. In 1867, he was asked to be a contractor for the planned extensions to Portsmouth Dockyard. This was an enormous £2.25 million scheme designed by Colonel Sir Andrew Clarke and superintended by the civil engineers Messrs. Henry Wood, J Macdonnell and Charles Colson of the Admiralty.

John Towlerton Leather was now in his sixty-third year. He knew this huge project, lasting a minimum of five years, would be too much to take on alone, so he decided to share the load in a joint venture. JTL's assets had certainly grown, both in the

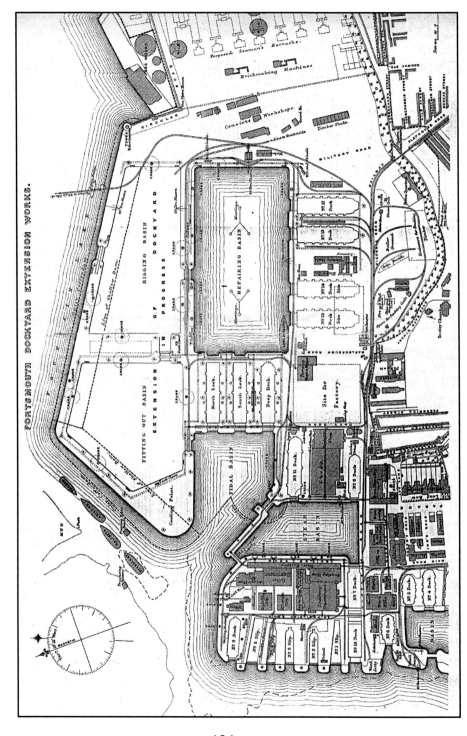

Plan of 'The Great Extension' at Portsmouth Docks (1867-1874) – a £2¼ million scheme. (Proc. ICE Vol 64, 1880-81, Charles Colson)

bank and in the large amount of plant he had accumulated, but he knew how easy it was for a contractor to lose capital when unforeseen problems arose. He also knew that, all being well, here was an opportunity for future income at a time when he would probably take a less active role in day-to-day work. He partnered with Mr George Smith of Pimlico as 'Leather and Smith and Co', joint contractors for the Portsmouth Dockyard Extensions. Initially, it was to be a five-year project, though it took considerably longer than this. Helping him at this stage was his youngest brother Charles James Leather who had come to live at Grounds Villa, Portsmouth and who often officiated when John Towlerton was absent. Another vital partner was Edward Pease Smith who had been a colleague and friend for over 30 years. As general manager, E P Smith of Portland Breakwater fame took an important part in designing some of the special equipment and temporary works, together with C H Meyer who also assisted the contractors. John Lillywhite was clerk of works.

The Royal dockyard at Portsmouth had been gradually enlarged until, from 1790, it spread across 95 acres. At the introduction of naval steam vessels, it needed further accommodation. In 1843 the steam basin on the north side of the yard and four large docks were constructed, requiring an additional twenty acres of land. These were opened by Queen Victoria in 1848.

Situated on the English Channel, the harbour was well placed to service and repair admiralty vessels. The port itself was chosen to be upgraded and refurbished in its role as a naval arsenal. There was still the supposed threat from the French, which had already given rise to the sea forts in the Spithead channel beyond the harbour. The dockyard was inadequate for the latest steam-driven ironclad ships, which were so long that there was only one dock large enough to take even one of them. There were now several of these iron-hulled super ships and new ones were being ordered and built. New docks and basins with special features were required as, for example, iron ships had to be cleaned of the encrustation of

The Steam dredger Goliah at work in June 1868 on the Great Extension. (Portsmouth Central Library)

shells, weed and barnacles more frequently than wooden ones. The great new plan to develop the harbour at Portsmouth was presented to Parliament by the Lords of the Admiralty in 1864. The necessary powers being obtained, the area of the dockyard would be trebled and 95 acres of new land would have to be reclaimed from the seabed. The whole scheme was a formidable challenge as far as the civil engineers and contractors were concerned. But the extensions were to be on such a big scale that in spite of a further large increase in the number of war ships in the rearmament programme, there would still be enough dockyard space for servicing the whole fleet[40].

The works were to be on the north side of the island of Portsea, east of the old dockyard, and extending to the gasworks at Flathouse, a distance of nearly a mile.[41] The total additional area was 180 acres, about half of which was to be reclaimed from tidal mudflats. On the north-west side there was to be a Tidal Basin with two locks leading to a vast rectangular Repairing Basin, a quarter of a mile long and twenty-two acres in area. A vessel requiring a dry dock could easily be moved into one of the four projected on the south side of the repairing basin. Vessels would then move to the Rigging Basin before transferring to the Fitting Out Basin. Here they could take coal on board from a coaling point and return to the tidal basin. In addition a deep dock was planned. Ships of a thirty-two foot draught would be able to move in or out of the docks at any state of the tide. The rigging basin and docks numbers 14 and 15 (except for the entrances) were not commenced until several years later as these were not part of the Leather-Smith contract. The length of wharfage would be trebled to some three miles. The new works entailed a seven-fold increase in the area of enclosed basins.

Work began on 30 April 1867 and the first part of the operation was to enclose the area from which tidal water could be excluded. The sea bed consisted of extensive mudflats uncovered at low tide, with between 10 and 25 feet of soft mud to deal with. Below this were the resistant clay and the occasional sandy layer of the London Clay formation (of Lower Tertiary age) dipping gently away to the south-west. At certain horizons the clay contained hard nodules, known as septaria, as well as sandy concretions, both of which were troublesome for the pile driving operations. Initially, the sea was kept out by constructing two temporary dams, an inner one where the sea was shallow and an outer main dam in deeper water. Between the two, the harbour wall was constructed. The temporary dams consisted of very simple sheet-piles

[40] *The Evolution of the Docks and Industrial Buildings in Portsmouth Royal Dockyard 1698-1914* by Dr R C Riley (The Portsmouth Papers, No. 44, Portsmouth City Council, 1985.)

[41] *Portsmouth Dockyard Extension Works*, by Charles Colson (Proceedings of the Institution of Civil engineers, vol. 64, pp118-148, 1880).

designed to resist only seven feet of water. They were 30 feet long and driven in from a flat barge, then supported from the side. The temporary dams worked well and were only removed when the harbour wall was completed.

In a paper about the temporary staging, C H Meyer[42] points out the 'treacherous nature of the mud'. He mentions that, on one occasion, where the mud formed a slope against the piling, it slipped disastrously taking part of the dam with it, which had to be replaced. He noted that when the sea was excluded, the mud was even more difficult to negotiate, as not even a boat could cross it. The only way to navigate it was to build wooden piers or staging. In order to excavate the deep mud, floating dredgers were

Working on one of the docks at Portsmouth. (photo Royal Naval Museum)

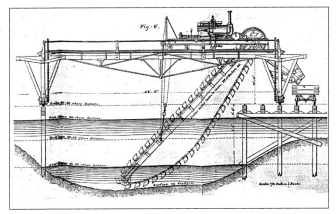

Drawing of the Travelling Steam Dredger. (Proc. ICE Vol 64, 1880-81, Charles Colson)

out of the question, and an attempt was made to dredge the mud from the staging. Edward Pease Smith worked on this to produce two light-weight steam dredging machines that operated from travellers with a 64 foot span. They dredged directly from the gantries, tipping the mud into wagons at the end of the travellers. This

---

[42] *Temporary Works and Plant at the Portsmouth Dockyard Extension*, by Christian Hendrick Meyer (Proceedings of the Institution of Civil Engineers, vol. 64, pp174-228, 1880).

worked well most of the time but the presence of peat and tree roots in the mud put too much strain on the system, and it soon had to be abandoned. The steam dredgers did a good deal of work, but the finishing off had to be done by man-power. The machinery wasn't wasted, however, but 'converted into an effective means for working inclines'[43].

An important feature of the temporary staging was a semicircular coffer dam which eventually would be closed to exclude the sea from the whole of the 73 acres site. It was 150 feet long and of 240 feet radius. Seventeen openings were left along its length, to be closed by lowering sliding panels into place. The system was the same as employed so successfully on the Middle Level Drain near Wisbech in 1862. When the time came the dam was closed in two tides, while earth was piled on the inside of the dam to give it more strength.

Two important features of the Portsmouth dockyard extensions – unusual during this period – were the general use of concrete, and the widespread application of steam power. Portland cement had been in use for only two or three decades and it was early days for making large amounts of concrete in big civil engineering projects. Tests were carefully carried out on gravel from different localities to ascertain the amount of space between the pebbles, and then, when these were filled with sand, what further space was needed for the finely powdered cement. Thus a ratio was arrived at: seven of gravel, to four of sand, to one of cement; and this ratio was used wherever normal concrete was required. Cement mortar for bricklaying was in the proportion of one part of Portland cement to two of sand. In planning the extensions in the early sixties, Sir Andrew Clarke was warned by other engineers that, in using concrete, he was employing a material of which little or nothing was known. However, he was convinced of its superior strength and thus became an early pioneer in its use.

The emphasis on steam power came from a combination of urgency – to get the bulk of the work done in the five years allotted – and the necessity of using staging, and therefore having a limited space in which to work. All routes across the mudlands used regular wooden viaducts carrying steam locomotives. There were normally eleven locomotives in use at any one time, each pulling about a dozen wagons. Thirteen tank engines were delivered during the four years from 1867 and 1871, most being new from JTL's Hunslet Engine works near Leeds. They were the usual 0-4-0 or 0-6-0 saddle tanks of eleven to sixteen tons used for shunting trucks up and down short stretches of line, and they were numbered No. 1 to No. 13. *Number One* was named *Lady Portsmouth* and was actually built at Manning Wardle's Boyne

---

[43] Obituary of Edward Pease Smith, *Proceedings of the Institution of Civil Engineers*, Vol. 52, p 285, 1877/78.

Engine Works in 1863. It had already done a stint at Waterloo Main Colliery and went to the Erewash Valley Iron Company in 1873. *Number 8* continued at Waterloo Main the same year, and *Midland* (No 2), *Gertrude* (No 3) and *Economy* (No 9) were sold on to John Aird and Sons, for further work at Portsmouth harbour.

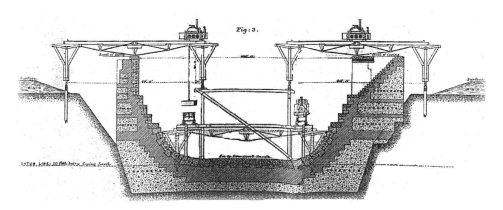

Cross-section of the North Lock showing gantries and travellers. (Trans. ICE Vol 64, 1880-81, Charles Colson)

Here there were seven or eight miles of railroad constantly in use, including four miles of wider track used for gantries. Steam travellers – large gantries that could carry overhead travelling cranes - were widely employed. They were built using wooden beams with a 64-foot span. They could manoeuvre heavy timber, lift boxes of a thousand bricks, move piling engines (with their steam up!) and carry loaded wagons. One of the most important items of steam machinery was the pile driver. The existing Sissons type was considerably modified to a new design, carried out by the three engineers, E P Smith, C H Meyer, and Ernest Latham. Altogether twelve of their pile-driving engines were constructed, and each was able to do twice the work of the older engines. They weighed over eleven tons, ran on rails and carried a ram of 22cwt. (see diagram). The speed with which the piling could be put in place was a measure of the progress of the works, so it was a vital though humdrum procedure. Steam engines were also in use for pumping, to keep the working area clear of water. Altogether, there were about seventy-five steam engines working at any one time.

Surplus mud from the excavations was carried along a wooden pier, out of the building site and across Fountain Lake, to be dumped on Whale Island. The pier interrupted a navigable channel, so a swing bridge was constructed – designed again by C H Meyer, E P Smith and Ernest Latham. It was made of wrought iron girders resting on a turntable in the centre of the channel, supported by a cluster of twenty-five piles. The bridge was operated from the centre by two men, who could swing it open in about half a minute.

In his comments at a meeting of the Institution of Civil Engineers (in February 1881), Sir Andrew Clarke congratulated the bold and liberal way the contractors had proceeded. 'It was astonishing to see so large an amount of temporary works executed before any permanent work had been attempted. This temporary work, however, secured the rapid, certain and economical construction of the whole of the permanent work. The contractors were men of considerable capital, and had the

Work in progress on the outer defensive wall at Coaling Point, looking north-west, and showing a large overhead steam gantry crane or crab. (photo Royal Naval Museum)

boldness to use it; for few men would have had the courage to expend on temporary operations which were not unattended with considerable risk and danger, close on a quarter of a million sterling, before commencing their permanent work'.

The foundations for the harbour wall were begun by excavating a trench, timber-lined, in the mud, whereupon 15-inch diameter piles were driven into the hard London Clay. On top of this, layers of concrete and brickwork were built up with a facing of Portland stone on the outer side. Two such walls were constructed and the 70-foot space between them then filled with hardcore. As each section of the harbour wall was finished, the temporary piling was up-rooted and the beech and softwood timbers used again on another part of the site. When complete there were 3,200 feet of harbour quays. In addition to this, 1,600 feet of quay walls were built round the Tidal Basin. Three large dry docks were constructed and the entrances to two further ones. Of these, docks 12 and 13 opened into the Repairing Basin and the deep dock connected with the Tidal Basin. Each dock was about 500 feet long by 100 feet wide, the floors being lined with large blocks of Cornish granite. The docks could be entered by ships with up to a 30-foot draft at any state of the tide.

Two large entrance locks were constructed connecting the Tidal Basin with the Repairing Basin, 80 feet wide at the entrance. The twenty-two acre Repairing Basin was the biggest basin of the dockyard and central to the new extensions. The prospective Fitting and Rigging Basins, each of fifteen acres, were not in the Leather-Smith contract and it was proposed to build these using convict labour (along with docks 14 and 15) after the contract was handed over to the Admiralty.

One of the biggest features of the extension works was the circular Hofmann's patent brick kiln, 112 feet in diameter with a huge chimney 140 feet tall. There were also two large 'Scotch' brick kilns with flat flues. Together they involved five steam engines, which prepared the high quality London clay, excavated on the spot, and formed it into bricks. In four years 70 million bricks were made, using the cheap labour of 850 convicts. It was anticipated that by September 1873 the works would be complete enough to allow water in.

In early March 1869, the foundation stone for the dockyard extensions was laid by Mrs Wellesley, wife of Rear Admiral G G Wellesley, CB. The ceremony took place at the entrance to one of the new docks. Among those present were civil engineers Mr Wood and Mr McDonnell, and Mr Lillywhite, the clerk of works. The contractors were represented by Mr E G Smith and Mr Charles Leather. Mrs Wellesley was presented with a silver trowel, and the immense stone was lowered to a depth of 27 feet 6 inches[44]. She pronounced the stone duly laid, while Admiral Wellesley wished the contractors success in the great work.

Looking back on the project the comment was made[45] that the substantial cofferdams and 'every other appliance requisite for the efficient execution of the work, were provided with a liberality and completeness which rarely been equalled, and which made an inspection of these works during the course of their execution one of the most noticeable engineering features of the period, and attracted numerous visits from engineers and other scientific persons, both English and foreign'.

---

[44] *Hampshire Telegraph and Sussex Chronicle*, Sat. 13 March 1869
[45] Obituary of John Towlerton Leather in *Proceedings of the Institution of Civil Engineers* vol. 83 p433-436.

Circular dam under construction in the Steam Basin. (photo Royal Naval Museum)

The contractors were very concerned about safety, and with some 2,400 men on the site and so much machinery in operation, they had reason to be. The safety record was relatively good, though accidents occasionally happened. The worst one in six years was on a Saturday in July 1873 when two workmen lost their lives and two were seriously injured. A temporary railway had been constructed across the entrance to the Steam Basin. It was twenty-five feet above the workings, supported by wooden stays. However the supporting stays had not been completed before a train of five loaded wagons backed onto the line. The line collapsed under the weight of the first two wagons dragging the other three and the engine with it, and the whole train was thrown to the bottom of the basin, 'piled in the utmost confusion'[46]. The two injured were John Bolton, the foreman, and William Houghton, the brakeman; while the engine driver, William Burden, and William Dudley, the rope-runner, were both crushed by the engine.

By 1871 the works were well advanced. JTL had always taken a certain pride in his own successes and achievements, and in the past he had celebrated, for example, by inviting his employees to a luncheon. He had entertained royalty and top political figures of the day. But now he had reached the peak of his career and perhaps soon would withdraw from active life as a contractor. He would show the world

[46] *Hampshire Telegraph and Sussex Chronicle*, Sat 19 July 1873.

his works, not on completion but during the more dramatic stages whilst still under way. The 'world' would be only those who could appreciate what he had done – the civil engineers themselves. He decided to invite the Institution of Civil Engineers and their president, Mr Vignolles, organising a special train from London to arrive directly at the great dockyard extension, and one of his own trains adapted with seats would take them round. Then perhaps a sit-down meal before they departed – all in grand style. The plan would be ideal for a summer's day in July. JTL was not one to put himself in the limelight, neither was he one for speechifying, but he was a great organiser and if he could get the Lords of the Admiralty to make the invitation, and if he asked all the civil engineers, the naval dignitaries and the civic gentry in Portsmouth, it could indeed be a grand occasion.

And so it was. On a fine Monday on the last day of July 1871, no less than 120 members of the Institution of Civil Engineers, including the president, Mr Vignolles, principal officers and students of the society, took their seats on a special train that left at 8 o'clock in the morning from Victoria station – on the London and Brighton South Coast railway. Nearly three hours later they arrived at a specially constructed platform at the Portsmouth dockyard where, waiting to meet them were Mr C Shaw Lefevre MP, Secretary to the Admiralty, Mr Walker, Accountant General of the Navy, Rear Admiral Loring CB, Admiral-Superintendent of the dockyard, Colonel W C Hadden of the Royal Engineers, and the Mayor of Portsmouth, J Baker Esq. Among the engineers were Colonel Andrew Clarke, chief engineer, Mr Henry Wood, executive engineer; and among the contractors John Towlerton Leather, his brother Charles Leather, George Smith, Edward Pease Smith, Christian Hendrick Meyer, John Lillywhite and as many others as possible.

The engineers were first entertained to a sumptuous breakfast in the mould workshop – catering was provided by Mr Houghton of Southsea Pier Refreshment Rooms. The visitors were given scale plans of the works to give a good idea of the extent of the operations, and were then divided into small parties to view the works – each group under the guidance of one of the contractors. There were a great array of top hats and JTL, tall and slim, must have looked seven feet tall in his stove-pipe hat. The 180 acre building site was vast, and a dozen railway trains each loaded with up to 50 wagons were continuously at work taking, earth and mud from within the dockyard area out to Whale Island; while others were hauling huge blocks of granite and Portland stone to be lowered into position. There were steam cranes, gantries, pile drivers, and dredgers, and upwards of two and a half thousand men at work. The whole arena of activity and enterprise looked very impressive.

Starting at the workshops at the south-west corner, the parties of civil engineers first proceeded along the new outer harbour wall, now over a mile in length, passing the massive walls of the new Tidal Basin. They looked out at the ships *Devastation*, an

Indian troop ship, *Serapis* and *Crocodile*, and continued to the seaward edge of the fitting basin. The visitors took particular interest in the resident naval ships *HMS Excellent*, a gunnery training ship, and the *Illustrious*. From here they descended the earth cuttings to examine the various mechanical and engineering appliances being used. They next went on to the Repairing Basin to look at the staging, engines, travelling cranes, and other machinery. There were twenty-four travelling cranes in use.

Most of the party were then conveyed around the works by a special train of trucks, fitted with padded seats for the purpose, which were pulled by one of the locomotives used for taking earth from the cuttings to Whale Island. There was some delay on the pier, caused by the continual passing of trains, worked by signals in the same way as an ordinary railway. Altogether, there was a total of thirteen miles of railway line in use. The visitors went on to see the brick-making where they were most impressed with this vast undertaking, carried on almost exclusively by 850 convicts. The large German circular kilns were particularly imposing. Some 70 million bricks had been made to date, one third of them having been used.

After three hours of inspection the visitors proceeded to the newly completed No 12 Dock, and to No 13 Dock, which had not yet been finished. On the floor of Dock 13, wooden planks were laid and on these an 80 foot sailcloth marquee had been erected, tastefully decorated on the inside with bunting, where the company were entertained to a magnificent cold buffet, Speeches of congratulations rang out all round. Even after this momentous gathering, the civil engineers still had to visit the steam engine factory, smithy, boiler shop and so on until, at seven o'clock, they thankfully boarded the special train taking them back to London.

Contractor Leather was not quite ready to retire yet. At the end of 1871, he had sold the Hunslet Engine Works for £25,000, and by December the following year had completed the contract for the Spithead Forts. But there were still decisions to be made and final work to be carried out at the dockyard. However, in June 1873, he had another triumph.

The Spithead forts and the dockyard extensions were more or less complete and the Channel Fleet was in occupation of the port. There was to be another great celebration when the Admiralty invited the Shah of Persia to visit Portsmouth to inspect the new Dockyard and review the Channel Fleet. Accompanying the Shah would be the Prince and Princess of Wales and their two eldest sons; Prince Arthur, the Duke of Edinburgh; the Grand Duke Cesarowitch and Grand Duchess Cesarevna, and the Shah's princes and princesses.

On a specially printed card, dated Wednesday 18th June 1873, and headed '19 Carlton House Terrace, London', an invitation went out to a list of distinguished gentlemen, including many civil engineers, to bring them to 'The Shah of Persia's Inspection of the Channel Fleet'. The Shah was also to see the dockyard extensions. On the reverse of the invitation card was a programme of arrangements: the big day was Monday, 23rd with a train leaving Waterloo station at 7.00am arriving at Portsmouth at 9.30. From Portsmouth station, guests would proceed to Mr Leather's office where refreshments would be ready. They would then 'board a Steamer to accompany the Royal Yacht to Spithead etc. the time for which is expected to be about 10 o'clock, and return to the dockyard for lunch about 2 o'clock'. JTL's next-door neighbour at Carlton House Terrace, Colonel Henry Byng, was to be present at the ceremony as Her Majesty's Groom in Waiting.

The day was a huge success. It was a bright summer's day when the royal train pulled in to the Portsmouth dockyard at 10.50 to loud cheers from the crowds. Their royal highnesses were welcomed by the Lords of the Admiralty; Sir Andrew Clarke, Director of Works and designer of the docks, and the Mayor of Portsmouth, Mr Davies. At 11.00am, to the sound of the Persian March and boatswain's whistle, the party mounted the red-carpeted gangway onto the royal yacht the *Victoria and Albert*. The yacht steamed out past the old wooden ships, the *Asia*, the *Donegal*, the *Duke of Wellington*, the *Victory* and *St Vincent*. These three-deckers were dressed with flags from masthead to bowsprit, and lined with sailors in blue trousers, white shirts and straw hats; and the first salute of the day was fired. The royal yacht was flying the royal standard of Persia, together with the Prince of Wales' standard on the mainmast, the Union Jack on the bowsprit, and St George's white ensign streaming from her taffrail. Moored on the wharf were the great, white-sided Indian troopships, the *Crocodile, Serapis* and *Euphrates,* also decked out with flags – and every naval officer in full dress.

The harbour was 'full of hulls and masts and men and flags now flying in the bright sun and the crowds that fringed the beaches were the setting of the whole picture'[47]. The royal yacht moved past the *Victoria* then the *Enchantress* carrying the Lords of the Admiralty. Then came the *Elfin*, the *Vigilant* (with some of the Shah's suite), the *Fire Queen* (Sir Roderick Mundy's yacht), and John Towlerton Leather and guests in his steam yacht – while church bells clanged from the shore. The *Tamar* had the House of Commons on board, the *Simoon* followed with the House of Lords, followed by the *Galatea* of Trinity House. There were twenty-one gunboats and, in the distance nearer to the Isle of Wight, were the Ironclads, twenty-three of them stretched out one behind the other in three long lines. As the royal yacht approached, a thunderous salute travelled from ship to ship, smoke and all. The Shah and Princes stood on the bridge and men aboard all the vessels cheered heartily.

[47] *The Times*, Tuesday June 24th 1873

The royal procession passed the great five-mast sailing ships, the *Agincourt* and *Northumberland* on the right, and the *Sultan* on the left. Further to the right was the shining armour of the *Hercules*, all looking most picturesque with their nettings and lines of marines on the poop[48].

Shah of Persia in 1873 on his first visit to Europe.

'The great anchorage was as crowded as a harbour, with mighty keels, steamers and yachts innumerable, and many beautiful private yachts moved about under steam or sail.' At one o'clock the royal party boarded the *Agincourt*, followed by the *Sultan*. While the Shah was on the deck of the *Sultan* many yachts gathered round and cheered. By 2.30pm the party had disembarked and went to lunch in a specially built pavilion. The Shah took coffee on the lawn, and at 4.30pm, the royal carriages drove to the dockyard where Sir Andrew Clarke explained to the Shah the new dockyard extensions. At 5.00pm the carriages returned and the Shah's party boarded the royal train to return to London. In the evening a grand ball was organised in the Assembly Rooms, decorated to look like the Arabian Nights, and among the guests were brothers J T and C J Leather. The orchestra was the stringed band of the Royal Marine Light Infantry from Gosport. It is not reported whether Messrs Leather danced the quadrilles, lancers and waltzes, but no doubt they enjoyed a day of great celebration.

A year later, by the summer of 1874, the Portsmouth Dockyard contract was complete and Contractor Leather's fifty-year working life was drawing to a close. He sold his plant and steam engines – much of it going to the Royal Engineers Department for further work on Portsmouth dockyard – and retired with grace and honour, prosperity and renown. He was seventy on 30 August 1874, a good time to turn his mind to his family and especially to his beloved Middleton estate to which he had added a

---

[48] Other ironclads included the *Glatton*, *Hotspur*, *Devastation* and *Royal Sovereign.*.

Middleton Hall showing the original farmhouse and the very large Tudor style new wing.

very large Tudor style wing, dwarfing the original farmhouse. He had also added a stable block and gatehouse entrance to the drive. In the next ten years JTL was to plant acres of forests, drain land, build more cottages and organise water supplies at Middleton. He was to enjoy several more shooting expeditions at this, his shooting lodge and holiday home, and to continue in public life as a magistrate. In 1875, as the Queen's representative, he became High Sheriff of Northumberland, an office he held for a period of twelve months.

Ten years later, on 6th June 1885, John Towlerton Leather, well into his eighty-first year, died at Leventhorpe Hall near Leeds. He left £256,000.

It may not have surprised him today, 200 years after his birth, that civil engineering is still governed by the same underlying principles; that his breakwaters and earth dams mostly survive and similar works are still being built (and that some still fail); that his iron bridges and lock gates have had to be replaced; that his railways are still in use, though new motive power has left behind the age of steam. Perhaps the most lasting and visible monuments to our civil engineer are the elegant Tadcaster viaduct and the solid Spithead Forts, and these may still be regarded in awe 200 years into the future.

JTL taking time for some reading in his well stocked library at Middleton Hall

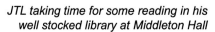

Index